Young Israel of Woodmere

47th Annual Dinner

Honoring

Rabbi Kalman and Jordana Topp
GUESTS OF HONOR

Martin and Rochelle Goldmark
AMUD AVODAH AWARD

Andrew and Tamar Sicklick
NEW LEADERSHIP AWARD

January 13, 2007
24 Tevet, 5767

Dedicated by

Dana and Jeremy Frenkel
Devora and Nathaniel Rogoff
Cheryl and Avi Savitsky
Tamar and Andrew Sicklick
Bonnie and Kenneth Sicklick
Patti and Michael Steinmetz

ArtScroll Halachah Series®

Rabbi Nosson Scherman / Rabbi Meir Zlotowitz
General Editors

RABBI AARON GLATT, M.D

VISITING

רפואה שלמה
Get
Well
Soon!

Published by

Mesorah Publications, ltd

BLUMENTHAL EDITION

ביקור חולים

THE SICK

A halachic and medical guide –
with down-to-earth advice

FIRST EDITION
First Impression . . . July 2006

Published and Distributed by
MESORAH PUBLICATIONS, Ltd.
4401 Second Avenue
Brooklyn, New York 11232

Distributed in Europe by
LEHMANNS
Unit E, Viking Business Park
Rolling Mill Road
Jarrow, Tyne & Wear NE32 3DP
England

Distributed in Israel by
SIFRIATI / A. GITLER — BOOKS
6 Hayarkon Street
Bnei Brak 51127

Distributed in Australia & New Zealand by
GOLDS WORLD OF JUDAICA
3-13 William Street
Balaclava, Melbourne 3183
Victoria Australia

Distributed in South Africa by
KOLLEL BOOKSHOP
Ivy Common 105 William Road
Norwood 2192, Johannesburg, South Africa

The author can be reached via e-mail at aglatt@pol.net

ISBN:
1-4226-0067-x Hardcover
1-4226-0068-8 Paperback

Printed in the United States of America by Noble Book Press Corp.
Bound by Sefercraft Quality Bookbinders, Ltd., Brooklyn, N.Y.

This volume is dedicated by

Beth and Reuben Blumenthal

to the memory of our beloved fathers,

Isidor Blumenthal, ז"ל

ר' יצחק בן יוסף ז"ל

and

Sidney P. Rosenblum, ז"ל

פנחס זעליג בן ישראל משה ז"ל

Isidor Blumenthal, ז"ל, dedicated his life to the mitzvah of bikur cholim. Over half a century ago, as soon as he became a member of the Far Rockaway community, he was a mainstay of its Bikur Cholim Committee, co-founded by Congregations Shaaray Tefila and Kneseth Israel (The White Shul). He loyally visited ailing neighbors — whether at home or in the hospital — on Shabbosim and Yomim Tovim, offering moral support and concrete assistance. His *eishes chayil*, Mrs. Ann (Chanchy) Blumenthal, שתחי', has always shared his devotion to bikur cholim. Inspired, younger generations have followed in his — and her — footsteps.

Sidney Rosenblum, ז"ל, in his own inimitable way, used his humor and congeniality to cheer those in need of a lift. Neighbors fondly recalled his visits and phone calls long after they occurred. To this day, his *eishes chayil, Mrs. Sylvia Rosenblum,* שתחי', pays weekly visits to neighbors who are ailing, cheering them with her warmth and optimism. Not surprisingly, two of their children chose the medical profession, enabling them to provide relief to those in pain.

We also dedicate this volume to the memory of

Gail Blumenthal, ע"ה

Lorraine Friedman, ע"ה

and

Sherry Garber, ע"ה

three courageous women who greatly appreciated the *chesed* of bikur cholim showered upon them by loving friends and relatives.

In the merit of this volume, written, at our request, by our dear friend Rabbi Dr. Aaron Glatt, may each and every *choleh* be granted a *refuah sheleimah*.

שמואל קמנצקי
Rabbi S. Kamenetsky

2018 Upland Way
Philadelphia, Pa 19131

Home: 215-473-2798
Study: 215-473-1212

י' בתמוז, תשס"ו

הנה שלח לפני הרב ר' אהרן גלאט, שהוא רופא מומחה וגם משמש
כסגן בבית הכנסת צעירי ישראל בוודמיר וגם בק"ק אנשי חסד ביולעט
בתור הסכמה לספרו בשם "Visiting the Sick" שכולל הלכות
והשקפות בעניני ביקור חולים ונלוה עם הספר פרקים מחתן אחי
הרה"ג רב אברהם שמחה לעפקוועיץ מרא דאתרא דק"ק אנשי חסד,
ובן אחי הרה"ג רב מרדכי ראש ישיבת תורת חיים.
והגם שמפאת טרדות לא עלה בידי לעיין ולברר כל הגליונות אבל
ברור לי ש"חזקה על חבר שלא יוציא מתחת ידו דבר שאינו מתוקן".
ע"כ אני מברכו בברכת ההצלחה ויזכה לחזק לבות אחנו בנ"י לקיים
מצות "הדרך ילכו בו" זו ביקור חולים בכל פרטיה ודקודקי'

בכבוד וברכת התורה

שמואל קמנצקי

The previous book of Rabbi Glatt M.D. was *Women in the Talmud*. It contains letters of approbation from eight prominent rabbis, in Israel and the United States.

ক Table of Contents

❧ Foreword

I am honored to write a few words in this *sefer* that has been authored by an incredible human being, Rabbi Dr. Aaron Glatt. All that he has written in this book — be it regarding halachah, medicine or sensitivity — is a reflection of his pristine personality. May the *Ribbono Shel Olam* grant that this *sefer* be accepted favorably by the public, and may its practical wisdom help thousands throughout the world.

I would like to share some thoughts that crystallize the essence of bikur cholim and the essence of this work. *Chazal* (*Yevamos* 79a) teach that Klal Yisrael can be recognized by the following three attributes: They are *rachmanim*, "compassionate," *byshanim,* "sensitive," and *gomlei chassadim,* people who grant favors.

When I saw this *Chazal*, I wondered about the order in which the attributes are listed. The first (being compassionate) and the last (doing favors) are characteristics that involve giving to others, hence they are similar. However, the middle attribute (being sensitive) is a personality trait of an individual. Why would it be juxtaposed between the other two? Seemingly, the two similar traits should have been placed next to each other; why the interruption in the middle?

I believe that *Chazal* wanted to remind us of something important while we are in the mode of being compassionate or doing favors. Remember the recipient! He or she is a sensitive person with feelings and pride. No one wants to feel that he is another person's mitzvah. Someone once told me, "I don't want to be your *lulav*!" *Chazal* teach us that Jews are sensitive and, therefore, although they may be in the hospital or incapacitated and homebound, this is not a reason for someone to treat them with less consideration, warmth and respect.

Visits to a *choleh* (and similarly, to mourners sitting *shivah*) should not be open ended! People and their families need their privacy. They can't be expected to "entertain" guests (yes, even you) for hours on end. No one should *ever* say to a *choleh*, "I think you have the wrong doctor; I can get you a better one." If you have a suggestion, make it to the family, not to the patient. No one should stay in a hospital room when a doctor comes to speak to a patient. Your right to visit does not grant you the permission to read hospital charts. And frankly the *choleh* does not have to, nor does he need to, hear about the times you were sick. These things may seem elementary, but you would be surprised how many well-intentioned people violate these basic rules.

Rashi (*Shemos* 22:24) picks up on this point. The Torah teaches: *When you will lend money to My people, to the poor person who is with you ...* Rashi is concerned about the extra words — *the poor person who is with you.* The verse could have simply told us about the rules of lending money without that phrase. However, Rashi explains that the extra words in the verse instruct us to "*Look at yourself as if you are the poor person.*" The lesson is sensitivity. When Hashem blesses any of us with the capacity to give, to teach, to heal, or to encourage, we must do so not with a feeling of arrogance *chas v'shalom*, but with a feeling of gratitude to Hashem that we are the givers and not the recipients.

Rav Chaim Shmulevitz in *Sichos Mussar* (Essay 8, year 5731) cites this Rashi and adds, "The 'giving' should be with honor and dignity. The giver should be sensitive to the feelings of the poor man in need of a favor. Appreciate his situation by putting yourself in his position."

I once heard an interesting insight in the name of Rav Velvel Soloveitchik, the Brisker Rav, regarding bikur cholim. The Rambam writes: One who visits the sick should pray for mercy on his behalf and then leave (*Hilchos Eivel* 14:6). Why does the Rambam state that after one asks for mercy he should leave? Is that an integral part of the mitzvah?

Rav Velvel felt that, indeed, leaving at the appropriate time is also part of the mitzvah. It shows a concern for the patient, that you are not trying to burden him with your presence (see also ibid. 14:4).

The reward for bikur cholim is enormous both in this world and the next. We say every morning: אֵלּוּ דְבָרִים שֶׁאָדָם אוֹכֵל פֵּרוֹתֵיהֶם בָּעוֹלָם הַזֶּה וְהַקֶּרֶן קַיֶּמֶת לוֹ לָעוֹלָם הַבָּא. וְאֵלּוּ הֵן ... בִּקּוּר חוֹלִים, *These are the precepts whose fruits a person enjoys in this world but whose principal remains intact for him in the World to Come ... visiting the sick.* *Chazal* teach (*Sotah* 14a) that it is our obligation to adapt for ourselves the characteristics of Hashem. Just as He performed bikur cholim (with Avraham Avinu after his *bris milah*), so too must we visit those who are ill.

The Rambam exhorts us to perform this mitzvah frequently, but with sensitivity and by not being a burden on the patient (*Hilchos Eivel* 14:4). I have often thought that *Refaeinu*, the blessing of healing in our *Shemoneh Esrei*, is the eighth blessing for a specific reason. The Maharal teaches that the number eight symbolizes something that is beyond nature — something that is extraordinary. May it be the will of Hashem that all those who are ill be healed from their maladies, even those that seem incurable, so that everyone will be able to function to his fullest potential.

And when that comes to be, we will read this *sefer* not as a practical guide, but as a work of halachah and *mussar* written simply for the sake of Torah learning. And Rabbi Dr. Glatt will then be able to give his wonderful Torah *shiurim* undisturbed and uninterrupted — and Klal Yisrael will gain immeasurably.

Respectfully,
Paysach J. Krohn
Kew Gardens, New York

❧ Introduction

It is with deep gratitude and *hakaras hatov* to the Almighty that I recite *Shehecheyanu* on completing this *sefer, Visiting the Sick,* a halachic and medical guide — with down-to-earth advice. In this practical compendium, I have attempted to elucidate the essential source materials for this important mitzvah, as well as to provide contemporary halachic opinion, coupled with very realistic guidelines for the practical performance of this mitzvah. Therefore, this *sefer* is divided into three sections.

The *sefer* opens with the **first section** containing several chapters providing very practical information on various aspects of bikur cholim — sensible suggestions for performing bikur cholim in the 21st century. The first chapter discusses medical issues and includes advice for preventing infection for both patient and visitor, safeguarding a patient's dignity, and using (if and when necessary) appropriate personal protective equipment. Other critical medical issues are discussed as well. Each of the next three chapters in this first section expresses a different point of view — that of the (1) rabbi/physician (written by myself); (2) patient; and (3) family of a sick child. My rabbi/physician perspective chapter provides detailed practical "DO's and DON'T's" — very specific guidelines on how to prepare for the visit, the visit itself, what to say and not say, how to act during the visit, and post-visit recommendations. The latter two superb chapters were guest authored by esteemed *rabbanim* who experienced significant illness (themselves or in their immediate family) and express their thoughts from their unique perspectives on "receiving" bikur cholim.

In the **second section**, I analyze some of the major *teshuvos* (halachic responsa) from three of our greatest contemporary sages — HaRav Moshe Feinstein *zt''l,* and *l'havdil bein chaim l'chaim,* HaRav Eliezer Waldenberg *shlita,* and HaRav Ovadia Yossef *shlita* — who have written extensively on the laws of bikur cholim. Because of space and time constraints, I have reproduced only a small fraction of their numerous and astute responsa in an abridged English translation. Each *teshuvah's* source is provided so that anyone who so desires can delve into it in its original Hebrew.

To fully understand any halachah, one must trace its origins to the original sources. Therefore, the **third section** of this book begins with the two major discussions in the Gemara dealing with visiting the sick. In the **fourth section** I translated the pertinent laws of bikur cholim as expounded by our principal halachic authorities: the Rambam, *Shulchan Aruch* and commentaries, *Chochmas Adam* and *Aruch HaShulchan.* Each of these halachic works is recorded first in its original Hebrew (or Aramaic), followed by an accurate, albeit not literal, translation of the material. This allows even those who have never studied these sources to follow the development of our bikur cholim rituals.

Needless to say, this book does not replace expert advice regarding specific situations and illnesses. On the contrary, I hope it will motivate readers to ask questions and seek out authoritative guidance from *rabbanim* and *gedolim.*

By gathering these sources — which span several millennia — into a single volume, I hope that men and women, teachers and students (especially those in high schools, colleges, yeshivos and seminaries), indeed, Jews of all ages and backgrounds, will gain worthwhile and useful information about bikur cholim. In addition, I hope that bikur cholim societies will find this *sefer* a useful resource for their holy work.

An editorial clarification: Throughout this volume, for the sake of simplicity, I have generally referred to both the *choleh* (sick person) and visitor with the masculine (generic) pronouns: he, him and his. Needless to say, unless otherwise stated, all laws and guidelines apply to both male and female patients and visitors.

The outstanding yeshivos and camps that I attended during my formative years provided the foundation upon which my *rebbeim* could build. Without the continuing influence and unbelievable Torah knowledge of my *rebbeim* — Rabbi Mordechai Willig *shlita,* Rabbi Hershel Schachter *shlita,* Rabbi Avrohom Wosner *shlita,* and Rabbi Yitzchak Knobel *shlita,* along with my "tape" *rebbeim,* Rabbi Moshe Meir Weiss, Rabbi Yissachar Frand, Rabbi Fischel Schechter, Rabbi Noach Isaac Oelbaum, Rabbi Berel Wein, Rabbi Yosef Viener and Rabbi Paysach Krohn *shlita,* among many others — this *sefer* would never have been possible. The tremendous *hakaras hatov* I owe my *rebbeim* is incalculable. Any Torah I have ever been privileged to give over is built upon what they have taught me. Rabbi Krohn deserves special thanks as well for graciously writing the beautiful foreword to the *sefer.* He truly fulfills the dictum: If you want something done well, give it to a busy person.

I am blessed to live near many *talmidei chachamim,* including *harabbanim shlita,* Rabbi Dovid Spiegel, Rabbi Mordechai Kamenetzky, Rabbi Doniel Lander, Rabbi Chanina Herzberg, Rabbi Shlomo Eisen, Rabbi Moshe Weinberger, Rabbi Dovid Weinberger, Rabbi Heshy Glass, Rabbi Yakov Feitman, Rabbi Moshe Katzenstein, Rabbi Mordechai Yaffe, Rabbi Aryeh Ginzberg, Rabbi Tzvi Flaum and Rabbi Shaya Richmond, who have always been available for advice and sage counsel. As importantly, Margie and I are privileged to enjoy the closeness of our siblings and their families, and many wonderful and dear friends, both here and in Eretz Yisrael. May Hashem grant them, among all of Klal Yisrael, health, safety and peace in these tumultuous times.

I once again thank ArtScroll, and specifically the incomparable Avrohom Biderman and Mrs. Judi Dick, along with Mrs. Mindy Stern, Mrs. Chumie Lipschitz, and Reb Moshe Deutsch, for their superb job in accepting the text and transforming it into a beautiful *sefer.* The exquisite cover is another one of Reb Eli Krohn's masterful designs, for which I am grateful. ArtScroll's enviable position in Jewish life is a tremendous credit to their founders, and it is a great *zechus* to be associated with them.

I would especially like to thank Rabbi Herschel Billet and Rabbi Kalman Topp of the Young Israel of Woodmere, and Rabbi Simcha

Lefkowitz of Congregation Anshei Chesed of Hewlett, and all the wonderful members of both of these great shuls, for allowing me to participate in Jewish communal life. These beautiful holy congregations have allowed me to grow spiritually, and provide me with a greater purpose in life. Thank You.

Many people were involved in bringing this *sefer* to fruition. Mr. Reuben Blumenthal has been a most praiseworthy sponsor, asking me to write it *l'illui nishmas* his dear departed father, Reb Yitzchak ben Yosef (Isidor Blumenthal), and his late father-in-law, Reb Pinchas Zelig ben Yisroel Moshe (Sidney P. Rosenblum). May Hashem bestow upon Ruby, his *eishes chayil* Beth, his mother Ann (Chanchy) Blumenthal, and their entire family His everlasting kindness. Mrs. Chava Willig Levy has served as a most outstanding editor; her handiwork is clearly present throughout this work. May Hashem continue to shine His blessings upon her. I also would like to thank Mrs. Gail Solow for her excellent transcription of my tapes.

Finally, *acharon acharon chaviv*, this *sefer* would never have been even remotely possible were it not for the tremendous *zechus avos* with which my wife and I have been blessed. Our parents, Anna and Joseph Glatt *shlita*, and Ethel and Marshall Korn *shlita*, have been unfailingly supportive. May Hashem grant them health and *arichas yamim v'shanim*, and may they see much *Yiddishe nachas* from their children, grandchildren and great-grandchildren, *kein yirbu*. May this *sefer* also be *l'illui nishmas* our grandparents, *zt"l*, whose love and devotion to Torah and Klal Yisrael shape us to this very day. I can never adequately thank my remarkable *eishes chayil*, Margie, and our wonderful children, Ephraim, Ari, Chavi and Chezkie (*bli ayin hara*), for their continued support and love during my work on this *sefer*. May it be Hashem's will that they be granted all of His blessings in this world, as well as their share in His Glory in the World to Come. May this *sefer* and its study be a *zechus* for a *refuah sheleimah* for all those who need it, and especially for Esther Ettel bas Rivah Raisha, *besoch she'ar cholei Yisrael*. Amen, *kein yehi ratzon*.

Aaron Eli Glatt
Tammuz 5766

Practical Bikur Cholim: Firsthand Perspectives

Author's note: The following four chapters provide different perspectives on bikur cholim — from the viewpoint of rabbanim who are respectively a physician, a patient, and a parent of a choleh. Each has written independently, without knowledge of what the others wrote. My only instruction was, "Give your personal thoughts on bikur cholim from your unique vantage point." Therefore, these chapters occasionally repeat an idea already expressed by another author — and this is ideal, as it demonstrates the universality of the thoughts and reiterates the importance of that idea.

This chapter was written by the author. He is writing from the viewpoint of a medical doctor who is an infectious diseases specialist. He has witnessed many acts of bikur cholim and their impact. In this piece, he shares his insights, expertise and advice so others can benefit.

MEDICAL ASPECTS OF BIKUR CHOLIM

M ost of this *sefer* outlines the importance of bikur cholim from a halachic point of view. This section will delve into some of the critical medical issues that arise from the performance of this mitzvah, issues of which both patient and visitor must be aware. The purpose of this section is not to dissuade or frighten people away from fulfilling this superlative mitzvah. However, as with all commandments, the more we know and understand the precept, the more optimally we can serve our Creator.

The importance of bikur cholim has been established throughout this volume. *Chazal* have stressed that it is an obligation to visit the sick, but only if the visits do not cause the *choleh* discomfort or suffering. Therefore, the first and primary focus of every bikur cholim visit should be to benefit the *choleh* and not, *chas v'shalom*, to harm him. This is both a halachic and a medical imperative. If there is any doubt regarding the benefit of the visit, appropriate rabbinical and/or medical authorities must be consulted to ensure that one upholds the overriding halachic and medical dictate, *primum non nocere* (above all, do no harm).

Depending on the illness and the treatment involved, a visit may cause significant detriment to the patient. This includes, but is not limited to, concerns of contagion from visitor to patient (as well as from patient to visitor), exhaustion of an already debilitated patient and embarrassment or mental anguish that the visitation may precipitate. Although these concerns cannot be overstated, most people are intuitively aware of the tremendous potential distress that visiting may trigger in some *cholim. Cholim* may not feel like talking. In fact, it may be painful for them to talk. They may be very embarrassed because of their physical appearance, bedclothes, possible body odor, poor hygiene, lack of appropriate grooming, physical pain, tubing or other medical devices, etc., all of which might make it difficult for the patient to benefit from the visit. Therefore, it is incumbent upon every visitor to use the most cautious common-sense approach when deciding whether his visitation is truly necessary and/or beneficial. One tends to think that it is the *other* people (e.g., doctors, nurses, technicians and other hospital staff members — not to mention inconsiderate visitors) who are disturbing the patient. From experience, however, I can attest to the fact that frequently it is the most well-meaning visitor who can cause the greatest distress, for example, by overextending his stay. One should not assume that, just because one is a close relative or friend, one's visit will automatically be welcomed, even though it may frequently be of great *chizuk* to the patient. When in doubt, one should ask the patient, close relatives and/or physicians outright if visitation is good or bad for the patient; one should respect the answer one receives and not presume to know better or to assume that he is the exception to the rule. I will not belabor this point since most people are quite aware — at least theoretically — of these guidelines. Just remember, please, that they apply not only to everyone else — but to you too! (Please also refer to the chapters on Practical Do's and Don't's.)

Having said that, I will focus on potential medical concerns to consider when visiting a *choleh*. First, however, a linguistic clarification is in order. The term "bikur cholim," literally translated as visiting the sick, also applies to visiting people who have medical, physical and/or psychosocial problems but who are not necessarily "sick": a child with a developmental disability (e.g., mental retardation), an exhausted person providing care for an elderly parent, an expectant woman on bed rest, a person whose mobility impairment renders him virtually homebound, to name a few. We must be mindful not to limit our concept of bikur cholim solely to hospitalized, critically ill patients. Nevertheless, the remainder of this chapter addresses issues relating mostly to members of this latter group.

Patients who are sick are often, but not necessarily, immunologically compromised ("immunocompromised") and therefore may be highly susceptible to various infectious agents, such as bacteria, viruses, fungi and/or parasites. Well-intentioned visitors who have relatively minor infections (which their bodies can fight without any difficulty) may unintentionally transmit them to a *choleh* and cause significant, and potentially even fatal, complications. Obviously, this depends largely on the severity of the *choleh*'s illness and many other factors too complex to delineate here. Suffice it to say that an individual with a cold (a virus) or other viral flulike symptoms should carefully ascertain whether his visit is safe and appropriate. Under most circumstances, the answer will be a resounding "No." A *choleh* is not a *cheftzah shel mitzvah* (an item with which one performs a mitzvah), like a *lulav* and *esrog* that must be picked up and shaken! It is forbidden to perform a mitzvah at the expense of anyone else, in this case, the *choleh*. However, when it is absolutely essential that a person with these clinical symptoms visit a *choleh*, appropriate precautions (which might include masking, gowning and gloving) are imperative. When in doubt, ask the physician. Needless to say, regarding the most severely ill or immunocompromised patient, one who is even slightly "under the weather" should visit only under the most extenuating of circumstances, and only after consultation with the physician.

Severely immunocompromised patients (i.e., whose immune system is malfunctioning, either because of their underlying condition or because of treatments such as chemotherapy or radiotherapy) are extremely susceptible to contagious illnesses that may be transmitted by a visitor. Under almost all circumstances, unless the *choleh*'s physician has permitted it, such patients should not be visited by anyone who is not feeling up to par. In such cases, one should fulfill the mitzvah of visitation via a telephone call, a letter or e-mail.

Among immunocompromised patients, there are various ranges of susceptibility to infection. Obviously, patients in protective isolation (e.g., "reverse isolation," designed to protect them from visitors with transmissible germs) should not be visited by anyone who does not meet the requisite guidelines or who cannot follow all of the precautions that are listed outside the patient's room. In this situation, every visitor must perform appropriate hand washing, gloving and gowning; no one is excluded, not even those who "washed at home" or showered before their arrival. Bacteria are present in cars, in public transportation and on hospital elevator buttons — one must wash one's hands immediately prior to entering the patient's room. Again, a prospective visitor must ask himself, "How essential is my visit? Am I in fact helping or hurting the patient?" Many quarantined patients are better served by not having visitors. A discussion with the patient, his family and/or his physician should determine what is best under these circumstances.

When a *choleh* is immunocompromised, there are no exceptions to the above rules. Anyone, no matter how healthy he feels or appears, can potentially transmit a serious infection, which can prove fatal to such an extremely sick patient. However, if a patient is not immunocompromised, all that a healthy visitor needs to do is wash his hands before entering and after leaving the room. Unless directly involved as a caregiver, one should not touch, explore or in any way handle the patient's bodily secretions, containers, tubes and personal hygiene items. The person who acts in that capacity should carefully wash his hands after every such encounter. Washing for 30 seconds with soap and water, or with an alcohol-based antiseptic without water, should be adequate. This is not intended to frighten anyone away from visiting those who are hospitalized or ill. It is good common sense and should be adopted in many other situations as well (e.g., before preparing food, after using bathroom facilities, etc.).

Up to this point, we have mainly discussed the risks of contagion transfer from the visitor to the *choleh*. Let us explore the risks of contagion transfer from the *choleh* to the visitor.

Assuming that the visitor is in relatively good health (none of this applies if the visitor himself is immunocompromised in any way; he should consult his physician before visiting other *cholim*), he still should realize that there are a few conditions that can cause a healthy person to become severely ill upon contact with certain contagious patients. For the sake of brevity, this discussion will focus only on conditions prevalent in the United States and other developed countries. Whenever concerns exist regarding possible communicability of the *choleh*'s disease, appropriate medical and, where necessary, halachic authorities must be consulted.

As a general rule, especially with the increasing emergence of resistant microorganisms (i.e., bacteria, viruses, fungi and parasites), one should always wash one's hands after visiting a sick patient (and, as noted above, before entering a sick patient's room). This is to prevent the visitor from acquiring resistant organisms which may be present on the patient's body, hands, clothing, linen and/or his surroundings. Although, in and of themselves, these organisms may not be more virulent (i.e., likely to cause disease) than those typically on everyone's body and on many surfaces, the infections they might cause could be that much more difficult to treat and eradicate. Therefore, as a general rule, one should always assume that sick and especially hospitalized patients are colonized with more resistant organisms, hence appropriate hand hygiene must be practiced. I reiterate, this can be accomplished by washing one's hands with soap and water or the alcohol-based sanitizing solutions for at least 30 seconds.

If a visitor comes into contact with any of the patient's secretions, or vice versa, he should wipe them away and wash the affected area. When these secretions are likely to come into contact with a visitor, appropriate "personal protective equipment" (PPE's) — such as gowns, masks, face shields, and/or gloves — should be worn. In consultation with the physician and/or family, the visitor must assess beforehand what personal protective equipment is necessary. *In general, for most patients, PPE's are not necessary.* However, when a hospitalized patient has been placed on certain types of isolation, they may be mandatory.

Certain infectious diseases may pose a higher risk of transmission, even to healthy individuals. They include tuberculosis, bacterial or viral diarrhea and herpes viruses. Herpes infections come in various forms — some more common than others — including chicken pox and shingles (both caused by Herpes zoster) as well as the Herpes simplex virus.

Tuberculosis (Mycobacterium tuberculosis) remains an extremely serious infectious disease problem throughout the world. Although one to two billion people worldwide have been exposed to it and potentially can "reactivate" and become acutely ill, the risk of encountering a truly contagious case of tuberculosis in the United States is relatively small. However, elderly and immunocompromised patients remain at risk for reactivation of prior tuberculosis or acquisition of the disease for the first time. If they contract the disease, they would become highly contagious to any visitor. If there is any suspicion that a patient has an active case of tuberculosis, his physicians must be consulted to determine what, if any, precautions are necessary for any and all visitors, including healthcare personnel. Active tuberculosis must be differentiated from latent tuberculosis (in which patients have a positive skin test but no signs or symptoms of acute tuberculosis). Latent tuberculosis poses no threat to visitors, who can perform the mitzvah of bikur cholim without concern.

Bacterial and viral diarrhea can spread from patient to visitor if the appropriate precautions are not taken. Patients with poor hygiene (because their illness prevents them from cleaning themselves) or soiled linen should be presumed potentially contagious. Subsequently, one should wash one's hands carefully before and after each visit and, if necessary, wear appropriate personal protective equipment. However, if one does not come into direct contact with the patient, their secretions or their linen, the risk of transmission is extremely low. Patients with diarrhea or any other potentially contagious illness should not be greeted with hugs and hand shakes; it is advisable to defer unnecessary physical contact.

Herpes viruses are probably the most common and potentially contagious infections that can be transmitted from patient to visitor. Herpes zoster causes chicken pox in people who have never been exposed to it before. Chicken pox can occur at any point in life, from early childhood to very old age. Once a person has been exposed, he usually will contract chicken pox, manifested by the typical rash, fever and malaise; in most otherwise healthy children, it will run its course in a week or two whereas adults may acquire more serious disease. Once such exposure has occurred, a person remains at life-long risk of a reactivation of Herpes zoster, which manifests itself as shingles. This well-known rash, usually confined to a strip (dermatome) of skin, can become more generalized, especially in patients who are immunocompromised. It is very important to note that people who have never been exposed to Herpes zoster can acquire chicken pox if they become significantly exposed to someone with shingles. However, those who have had chicken pox cannot contract shingles from someone with chicken pox or shingles. This is because their own previous exposure prevents them from now contracting either chicken pox or shingles. Whether a person will ever manifest shingles depends on numerous variables; medical science has no accurate way to predict who will develop a case of shingles during his lifetime, but shingles is not contracted by re-exposure to Herpes zoster.

Therefore, it is essential that a person who has had no known exposure to chicken pox (and no blood test evidence of ever being exposed to Herpes zoster) should not visit anyone who has chicken pox or shingles. In this case, there is an excellent chance of transmission from the patient to the visitor. Although chicken pox in a child or adolescent is rarely fatal, it is quite serious and potentially fatal in adults, who should avoid exposure to it at all costs. A chicken pox vaccine is available, as is a newly licensed shingles vaccine; an adult who has never had the virus, especially if he regularly visits hospitals (where exposure to Herpes zoster is more likely) or is around young children, should ask his physician whether vaccination is appropriate.

Contact with blood is a serious risk of which everyone involved with bikur cholim should be aware. Regardless of the diagnosis, a patient's blood and/or bloody discharges should always be considered highly contagious. *Again, this is regardless of the patient's clinical illness and/or background.* Under no circumstance should such blood or bloody bodily secretions be handled without appropriate personal protective equipment. Should one come into contact with such blood or bloody secretions, the affected area should be washed immediately and professional advice should be sought to determine if additional evaluation is necessary. Fortunately, in the course of a typical non-professional bikur cholim visit, contact with blood will almost never occur. One should *not* be concerned about visiting patients because of this potential exposure.

For those who regularly visit hospitals or sick individuals — and certainly for those providing healthcare of any sort — vaccinations and other measures should be taken to maintain optimal health and to minimize the risk of inadvertently acquiring or transmitting infections. Current vaccines prevent (albeit not totally) hepatitis A, hepatitis B, pneumococcal and meningococcal disease, influenza, Herpes zoster and many routine childhood viral diseases.

It is beyond the scope of this chapter to delineate all the measures to be taken by those who interact with sick people. Although we firmly believe that *HaKadosh Baruch Hu* will protect those who are performing a mitzvah, we are not allowed to rely upon His protection when readily available measures can safeguard one's life. Above all, we must remember the dictum: *U'shemartem m'od es nafshoseichem* (And you shall carefully safeguard your health).

Finally, I would just like to add one very important general caution. Individuals must be extremely wary to avoid doing anything medically or halachically wrong, *chas v'shalom*, while performing the mitzvah of bikur cholim. This will be greatly expounded upon in the practical "Do's and Don't's" chapter, but for now, one *must be very careful NOT to*

(1) disturb or wake other patients or their visitors;

(2) read a patient's charts without permission;

(3) behave boisterously or inappropriately;

(4) prevent or hinder the physicians and hospital staff from performing their duties;

(5) transmit private or personal information without permission;

(6) do anything that may cause a *chillul Hashem* (desecration of God's Name).

Keep in mind that there are hospital staff members everywhere and they constantly observe the way visitors behave. Please, *DO* make *every* effort to maintain a pleasant demeanor; be courteous and polite when interacting with the custodial and professional staff, as well as other visitors and patients. Making a *kiddush Hashem* (sanctifying God's Name) is a magnificent way to increase the likelihood that a *choleh* will have a speedy recovery. May the *zechus* (merit) of our learning about bikur cholim, combined with our enhanced performance of this wonderful mitzvah, help bring about a *refuah sheleimah* for all *cholim.*

BIKUR CHOLIM:
25 PRACTICAL APPLICATIONS
OF THE HALACHAH

In this *sefer,* I have tried to translate and explain the words of the Talmud and noted halachic *sefarim* so readers can learn "inside" the laws and requirements of the mitzvah of bikur cholim. Despite knowledge of halachah, however, it may still prove difficult to transform this theory into actual practice. There are many situations where the halachic regulations are clear, but the circumstances make their application blurry. Thus, this chapter will be a practical "DO'S and DON'T'S" of bikur cholim, based upon my experiences as a physician caring for patients for nearly 25 years, and also as a rabbi. While these recommendations are primarily geared for hospitalized patients, most are equally applicable to patients at home or in rehabilitation or nursing home settings. These rules are designed for visitors, but often are applicable to all who are involved with the *choleh* on a day-to-day basis; in all instances, common sense must always prevail.

The purpose of this section is not *chas v'shalom* to deter anyone from accomplishing this colossal mitzvah, but to assure that the mitzvah is performed optimally. When in doubt, as always, ask a Rav how to proceed.

☙ *Preparing for the Visit*

---

1. Above all remember that visiting someone who is sick is only a mitzvah if the patient desires visitors. *Never* automatically assume that a patient wants to have visitors. Even if most people under similar circumstances would enjoy visitation, a specific individual may not want company. He may be embarrassed, in pain, uncomfortable, just want privacy or need to rest. *Always* call before visiting, unless you are the immediate family (spouse, parent, child) and expected to be there. Even then, calling ahead is invariably a good idea. Patients need rest, and as much as they would love to see you, they may not be up to it at the time it is convenient for you to visit. With regard to phone calls — try to ascertain when is a good time to call. Patients often have very hectic and erratic schedules. It is not unlikely that a patient may finally have fallen asleep (even in the middle of the day), maybe with the aid of a sleeping pill, and your call may awaken him. If you do call and the phone is not answered, do not repeatedly call back every few minutes — try again later. I advise patients to take the phone off the hook if they truly do not want to be disturbed.

Many patients, especially very young children, elderly patients with diminished mental capacity, comatose or non-communicative patients are often unable to verbalize their desires regarding bikur cholim. In these cases, if the family/caretakers believe that bikur cholim visits are in the patient's best interests, by all means visit. As we discuss later in this *sefer*, bikur cholim is a multi-purpose mitzvah. Even if the patient is incapable of communicating with you, your presence can provide benefits on numerous spiritual and practical levels, plus it may relieve or assist the overburdened caregivers. It is also an important reminder to the sometimes detached health care provider that there are caring friends and family who remain very concerned with the well-being and outcome of the patient.

Terminal patients, whether still in an acute care hospital, in a hospice type setting, or at home, need very special and complex bikur cholim considerations. The proper approach to caring for them is well beyond the scope of this book, and there are many wonderful publications that deal with this very specific population (e.g., *Death and Dying* by Rabbi Maurice Lamm). Nevertheless, one should certainly make every effort to visit/communicate with such patients if they are up to visitation.

2. When the patient, family or physician says don't visit, please obey their wishes — don't visit. Never assume you are the exception to the rule. (Kindly review the section on infectious risks/medical reasons not to visit, p. 21). Remember, you are not the only visitor; your visiting just for five minutes may be the 20th "just 5 minutes" of the day. If a patient really wants or needs to see you, he can readily spread the word.

3. Bikur cholim can be accomplished in many ways that do not necessarily involve your physical presence. Calling (not too early or too late) the patient or family and inquiring about his condition, spirits, etc., davening, offering to help with errands, children, meals, etc. are great ways to partially fulfill the mitzvah. E-mailing (or using the good old-fashioned postal service) is a fantastic way to stay in touch and to show how much you care, yet does not risk disturbing a sleeping patient or intruding upon pressing needs or tests. Many patients have told me how much it meant to them to read cheery upbeat e-mails from friends and acquaintances, and how grateful they were not to be burdened with talking to/seeing each of these well wishers. *Always* indicate in your note that the patient should not feel obligated to respond. And mean it — keep writing even though you have not received a reply.

4. I firmly believe that it is a good idea for one who is very sick, especially someone who is acutely ill, to appoint one family member or a close friend to be the contact person for visitors, well-wishers and friends. This "spokesperson" can relay updates and information on a regular basis, so that the patient is not burdened or disturbed excessively. (Again, e-mails are a great way to easily disseminate information broadly, rapidly, and inexpensively.) Needless to say, any information given out *must* be provided only with the permission and approval of the patient or (if he is not able to express his wishes) that of the family.

5. When a visit is "scheduled," make sure it complies with the hospital visiting regulations; if not, check if special permission has been obtained. This will prevent a *chillul Hashem*, staff annoyance and bad feelings all around, and will allow the visit to fulfill its purpose. It is very important not to antagonize the hospital staff, as this might possibly engender substandard care for the patient, the diametrically opposite intent of your bikur cholim visit.

≈§ The Visit

6. Once a visit has been arranged, offer rides to those individuals who are regularly with the patient and may have no other way to get to or from the hospital. This is especially helpful for relatives sleeping over at the hospital or in a bikur cholim apartment who need one-way transportation. Offer to bring specific items such as foods or snacks that are medically acceptable, tapes, books, magazines, *sefarim*. Do not hesitate to ask the sick person if he has any specific requests. Do not bring live flowers or plants, breakable/odorous/large objects; do not bring young children unless specifically told to do so. Many hospitals have age restrictions — if you are bringing children make sure they meet the hospital requirements. These suggestions can be modified for nursing home or at home bikur cholim, but as always, use common sense and inquire beforehand.

7. Leave adequate time to find parking and to locate the patient. Modern hospitals are massive and mazelike, patients' rooms are sometimes switched at a moment's notice, and patients are often taken for not previously scheduled tests in different hospital locations. Do not become annoyed and take out your frustration on the patient or staff. Do not pay a bikur cholim visit when you are pressured or rushed. The patient can sense your tension. Although it is wise to keep your visit brief, it is unwise to keep looking at your watch because you are preoccupied by something else. Bikur cholim is not a mitzvah to be "*chapped*" or "gotten over with."

8. *Never* enter a patient's room without quietly knocking, or asking the nurse to make sure it is okay to go in. I have seen many patients surprised (and horrified) by unthinking visitors who suddenly appear in their hospital rooms. Visitors may unintentionally enter when patients are in various stages of undress, dishevelment, caring for personal hygiene, or while they are being examined by physicians. No one would ever dream of entering someone's house, and certainly not their bedroom, without permission, yet visitors neglect this most basic courtesy in a hospital or nursing home setting. Hospitalization tends to rob patients of their modesty and privacy — do not contribute in the slightest to this very real problem.

9. Amazing as it sounds, I have seen visitors, in their zeal to do bikur cholim, wake a sleeping patient! *Never, ever, disturb a resting patient, unless you were specifically* told *by the patient* to wake them when you arrive. Do not feel terrible that you *shlepped* all the way to the hospital only to find the patient asleep and therefore you could not visit with him. Leave a note with the nurse to indicate you were there, and that you cared, quietly say a short prayer for the patient's well-being and complete recovery — and then leave quietly. In *Shamayim,* you get full credit for the visit — don't blow it by waking the patient!

10. Frequently, there are two (or more) patients in a room. Please don't forget that the other person in the room (whom you are not visiting) is a (sick) person too! Say hello, ask how he feels, wish him well. It takes only a second and may make a world of difference to them. It will definitely be a *kiddush Hashem*. Doing this will undoubtedly ease any tension in the room and go a long way in making the roommate more comfortable and friendly with the person you are visiting, which is beneficial for all concerned. And finally, and most importantly, it *also* is a mitzvah of bikur cholim!!! And isn't that why you came to the hospital? Many patients never have any visitors — think how wonderful it is for them when you pay them some attention.

11. While visiting your friend/patient, don't hog the room — leave chairs and space for the other patient to breath, live and have his/her own visitors. If "your" patient is well enough to walk to a lounge where there is more room, go there to spend the time of your brief visit. It may allow for more comfort and privacy for your visit, and it might be beneficial to everyone. Never sit on a patient's bed (unless specifically told to do so and it poses no medical concern), never read the charts, and make sure you leave the room immediately if there is a medical need to do so (i.e., their physician or nurse comes by).

12. *Never* enter areas or rooms on the floor that are out of bounds to visitors. Hospital pantries are for staff use only, unless otherwise indicated, and the laws of *geneivah* (theft) and *chillul Hashem* are applicable if you use something without permission. Don't look into other rooms as you stroll the halls. Make sure conversations and visits are not loud, excessively boisterous or rowdy. Tidy the public lounges and areas where you have made a mess, and turn off cell phones if signs indicate you should!

13. *Never* overstay your welcome. The best bikur cholim visits are the shortest, unless you have been explicitly asked to stay with a patient for an extended period of time or overnight. If you wait for the patient to suggest he is tired, you have been there far too long. A good rule of thumb — the sicker the patient, the shorter the visit. This is especially true of critical care areas (ICUs, CCUs) where the presence of visitors often impacts the ability to provide necessary medical and nursing care.

14. An excess of visitors at one time may be difficult and detrimental for the patient and the hospital staff. When other visitors enter, unless you likewise *just* arrived, take this as an indication that you should leave. This is especially so if the other visitors are close relatives or distinguished *rabbanim,* with whom the patient surely wishes to spend private time. Your presence may impede critical personal discussions. Pleasantly say your good-byes and leave, knowing your departure is a mitzvah too.

When permissible, bikur cholim on Shabbos presents additional halachic considerations. It is beyond the scope of this *sefer* to address the care of the sick patient on Shabbos, and visiting and certainly providing any type of care on Shabbos presents serious halachic questions that involve potential *chillul Shabbos*/lack of Shabbos observance. Being sick does not automatically override Shabbos laws, and every situation is not *pikuach nefesh*. It is always best to try and preempt problems by discussing these issues with a Rav before they occur.

◄§ What to Talk / Not to Talk About While Visiting

15. Many individuals feel uncomfortable when visiting sick patients, especially if the illness has recently been diagnosed or its onset was sudden and unexpected. That is normal and acceptable. Silence is not always golden, but it is far better than saying the wrong thing. Try and plan in advance appropriate things to say or discuss with the sick person so there will not be too many awkward pauses. Silence is not necessarily uncomfortable and does not always serve as an indication that you are ill at ease.

If the patient is comforted by your presence, without any conversation, the mitzvah of bikur cholim can be fulfilled by holding or stroking the patient's hand so that he/she feels your caring and compassion.

16. Remember that part of the purpose of the visit is to cheer up the sick person. Be prepared to tell a joke, a good story, and/or happy news that will perk up his spirits. In a *beis shivah* (house of mourning) one is not permitted to speak about things other than the dearly departed — we are not supposed to try and "distract" the mourners from their discomfort and sadness. The same is NOT true for bikur cholim. Anything you can do that will bring a smile to the patient's face, relieve him of his depression and pain (even if only momentarily) is wonderful. If the sick person wishes to discuss his illness, then listen attentively. However, the mitzvah of bikur cholim does not include, nor does it give the visitor the right to inquire about every detail and aspect of the illness. Indeed, that may be detrimental and cause anguish to the patient. Let the patient decide how much information he wishes to dispense regarding the illness. Never pry. Remember, the patient should feel better, not worse, after your visit!

Similarly, a *"geshmak"* (juicy) piece of gossip or *lashon hara* may bring a smile to the patient's face, but certainly will not help his spiritual and physical health.

17. The last thing a patient wants to hear about is how your Aunt Sadie or Uncle Morris had the same thing. And died. Painfully. Misery does not love company if that company is pessimistic, depressing and morbid. I would strongly suggest not inundating the patient with similar tales of woe as part of a feeble and misguided attempt to commiserate. Your excruciating backache is not the same as their bone cancer pain; your stomach ache is not their intestinal perforation. Let the patients speak about their illnesses (if they choose to do so) without playing "I Can Top That." Of course, if you really have had the same illness, you may be a truly wonderful source of inspiration and hope. Nothing can improve a patient's hopes and prospects more than seeing someone who had the same illness walking and talking and ensuring that you too will get through it. Just remember who is the patient now — and try to present as positive an image as is realistic and appropriate.

18. I have found that every patient differs with regard to talking about his or her illness. Some love to fill you in on sordid painful details; others are very private. To each his own. You must intuitively feel out what the sick person does and does not want to share about his illness. Never probe or ask too personal a question unless you are absolutely certain you should. And then think it over again and don't! If you are so close to the sick person, or you have special knowledge about his condition (i.e., you are an expert in that field, had the exact same problem, etc.) the patient will ask you for your opinion, if he wants it. And remember that anything the sick person tells you in a moment of deep personal revelation is to be treated as a most confidential statement, and is certainly not to be passed along as a juicy piece of news to which only you have been privy.

Also remember that the desires, needs and wishes of a patient are potentially in very dynamic flux. The sick person can quickly *b'ezras*

Hashem improve, and suddenly want more visits, or he can *Rachma-nah litzlan* get worse and visits are less helpful, or vice versa. Today he may have been in a garrulous outgoing mood and longed for company that never showed; tomorrow the opposite may be true. Don't assume that the conditions that were present today regarding bikur cholim automatically apply tomorrow. Keep in close contact with the appropriate family "spokesperson" to gauge what the current situation and needs are regarding visiting and all other aspects of bikur cholim.

19. Sick people are people too. Ask about their children; ask about their interests (learning, sports, hobbies); ask what you specifically can do to help. General offers of help are nice but of little practical value. Offer specific things — I would like to go shopping for your family tonight; I would like to pick up your children for carpool; I can bring over supper tomorrow; I can help your children with homework. Phrasing such offers as if they are a fait accompli may also make patients more comfortable accepting such *chesed* — which they would normally not take for fear of imposing on others. Remember that while the sick person is going through the physical pain and suffering of his illness, the entire family is greatly distressed and overly stressed as well. I am known to say: **"My patient is infected, but the whole family is affected."** I believe the mitzvah of bikur cholim is therefore potentially applicable to the whole family, since they too are "sick." And indeed, the benefits that the sick person receives knowing that his/her family is being helped through the difficult times are truly of immeasurable assistance to the patient's positive outcome. This *menuchas hanefesh* is certainly a fulfillment of bikur cholim.

20. Please resist the temptation to criticize the care/physician/hospital/medication that the patient is receiving. Unless you are truthfully a healthcare expert in the particular field of that patient's illness, you are in all probability not knowledgeable enough to provide a critique of the care with which the patient is being provided. All you will realistically accomplish is to undermine his faith in the caregivers. If he is making reasonable "*hishtadlus*" (effort) in combating his sickness, your imput is probably unnecessary, and can prove detrimental. I have seen many patients shaken and bewildered by well-intentioned visitors who confused them and undermined their trust in their institution or physician. Physicians, nurses and other "healthcare" friends especially fall into this trap. That is not to say that erudite visitors should not speak with a close relative and carefully impart their concerns. Knowledgeable friends can make the difference between life and death. They certainly should be encouraged to speak up and provide critical healthcare information that the family does not know. However, this must be done very carefully, constructively, and with the sole desire to make the family aware of other potential treatment options.

Always be extra careful about talking in the presence of a sleeping, debilitated or comatose patient. Medical science really does not understand "coma," and numerous firsthand accounts exist of patients being able to recall verbatim conversations that transpired around them while they were under anesthesia, comatose or incapacitated. A smart rule of thumb is to never say anything you would not say if the patient were awake, alert and able to hear.

21. After your brief visit is over, make sure you state that Hashem should grant the patient a *refuah sheleimah*, re-offer specific assistance that you can provide (to them or their family), and then leave. Teary drawn out good-byes are emotionally difficult for the sick person, and rarely provide any comfort.

22. When you leave, thank the nurses, clerks and other hospital staff for the care they are providing. They will certainly be appreciative, it is a *kiddush Hashem*, and it may result in better overall care for the patient. A box of candy or cookies for the staff is a nice tangible way for the family to show their appreciation when a patient is hospitalized for a long period in the same unit.

23. Never speak with the physician without the patient's expressed permission. Aside from the "HIPPA" (privacy) regulations mandating that it is illegal for the doctor to discuss the case with you without such permission, why would you do this! Even if you are a family member, the physician-patient relationship is private, and you have no right to request or obtain information unless the patient specifically permits this. I know many patients who were very upset that close family and even close friends asked for private information, and sometimes received it.

Furthermore, physicians are very busy and only human. Speaking multiple times to different family members can be quite frustrating. A dedicated physician recently confided to me that he disliked going to the ICU to care for one particular patient because different family friends and relatives consistently bombarded him regarding information he had already provided. Aside from the frustration factor, physicians may use slightly different terminology when speaking with different family members, unintentionally imparting dissimilar impressions, confusing the situation. I strongly suggest that when the patient is not capable of speaking with the physicians, a *single* family member should be designated to convey information to and from the physician. No one else should contact the physician. If everyone wants to hear the words directly from the doctor, then arrange a time convenient for everyone to gather and hear news directly from the physician, and to ask questions. But it is unrealistic to expect physicians to sit at different times with different family members and/or friends and to repeatedly convey the same information.

24. Never ask physician friends of the patient (who may be aware of private information) to provide you with inside details and results of tests. This is illegal and places the friend in a terrible bind. I can't recall how many hundreds of times people have asked me how someone is doing, and then they follow that up with specific detailed questions. While I understand their well-intentioned motives and true interest in our mutual friend, they are asking me to break the law or go behind the back of our sick friend and provide them with information to which they are not entitled.

✌ Post Visit Follow-up

25. Always follow through on the kind offers of aid you promised, especially in regard to care of children, cooking, transportation, or services directly for the *choleh*. The patient cannot be expected to call and remind you; he may not even remember who promised what after his long day of treatment, visitors and emotional distress. Never offer that which you don't truly intend to do; do not forget to follow through promptly, responsibly, and without expectation of reward or honor. If you performed some service for which you expect to be reimbursed, keep a record of it, and unless you are in desperate need of the money yourself, hold off asking for payment till a more propitious time.

Remember that bikur cholem does not stop when the patient is discharged. Indeed, there may be even more need then for friends to assist with activities of daily livings, errands, doctor follow-up visits, etc.

Call, write, e-mail and/or visit again as soon as appropriate after the initial visit. Remember, there is no maximum *shiur* that you can exceed, as long as you are benefiting the patient. Every time you perform the mitzvah of bikur cholim you are doing a wonderful *chesed*. By learning the halachos, and by following the above practical guidelines, may we be *zocheh* to see all sick people merit a *refuah sheleimah* from Hashem.

HOW TO COMFORT A PATIENT

Rabbi Simcha Lefkowitz
Rav of Congregation Anshei Chesed,
Hewlett, NY

Three years ago I experienced an unusual serious condition that incapacitated me for a period of time. With Hashem's help, the support of my wife Shoshana, my family, friends from Congregation Anshei Chesed and others, I have been able to recuperate and return to my regular life activities. Both during this period and after, I reflected on what was said to me by well-wishers, and I sought insight and comfort from the words and teachings of *Chazal*. I would like to share with you some of what I have learned as a result of this experience.

I have struggled for many years to understand fully the meaning of the *berachah* we give to every *choleh*, "May you have a *refuah sheleimah*, May you be healed completely." Why is it necessary to specify *"sheleimah"*? Would anyone wish for a *choleh* to be healed only partially? What is a *refuah* that is not *sheleimah*?

One morning during davening, the meaning of this phrase became very clear to me: When you become seriously ill, the sickness attacks your body physically and your *neshamah* (soul) emotionally and spiritually. Inevitably, there are feelings of depression, anxiety, tension and a lessening of *bitachon* and *emunah*. These emotions attack your soul, your *neshamah,* in complex ways. Often the *choleh*

This chapter is written by a noted community Rav, an educator and accomplished *talmid chacham* who has helped many people. He is writing from the perspective of a patient who experienced serious illness. May Hashem continue to bestow His *berachah* upon him and his family.

is healed from his physical disease but continues to be plagued with many difficulties due to his *"neshamah* illness." This aspect of the illness can be longer-lasting and more insidious than the physical sickness. So, when you wish someone a *refuah sheleimah*, be aware of what you are saying! When visiting a *choleh*, there may not be much you can do to help him physically, but there are many levels and types of healing that you can bring for his spiritual "sickness." The friendly conversation, the *tefillos*, the singing, the jokes, and the balloons are all available without a prescription. The *mevaker* with a caring heart can effect real changes in the *choleh*'s *neshamah*.

ـهٔ Comforting the Choleh

The question of how to comfort a *choleh* and how one should act when visiting a *choleh* is one that requires great sensitivity and deep thought. The usual conversational approaches might be acceptable for people with minor or temporary problems, but these need to be modified in consideration of the *choleh* whose situation is more severe. Only someone who has been on the receiving end of such remarks can understand firsthand the positive and negative impact they can have.

One type of statement that is well-meant, but actually quite detrimental is, "See, someone else has it bad too," or "So-and-so has it worse than you." Other damaging comments to a *choleh* are a visitor's reports that someone has recently died, or someone else is still sick, or another has had a heart attack. The visitor's intention is to make the *choleh* feel stronger in comparison or to make him understand how fortunate he should feel that he is not as ill as "So-and-so." In reality, these statements have the opposite effect, causing a *choleh* to feel even worse. Why?

Consider this story found in the 14th chapter of *Avos D'Rabbi Nassan*:

כשמת בנו של רבן יוחנן בן זכאי נכנסו תלמידיו לנחמו. נכנס רבי אליעזר וישב
לפניו וא"ל רבי רצונך אומר דבר אחד לפניך א"ל אמור. א"ל אדה"ר היה לו בן ומת
וקבל עליו תנחומין. אף אתה קבל תנחומין א"ל לא די לי שאני מצטער בעצמי אלא
שהזכרת לי צערו של אדה"ר.

נכנס ר' יהושע וא"ל רצונך אומר דבר אחד לפניך א"ל אמור. א"ל איוב היו לו
בנים ובנות ומתו כולם ביום אחד וקבל עליהם תנחומין אף אתה קבל תנחומין. א"ל
לא די לי שאני מצטער בעצמי אלא שהזכרת לי צערו של איוב.

נכנס ר' יוסי וישב לפניו א"ל רבי רצונך אומר דבר אחד לפניך א"ל אמור. א"ל
אהרן היו לו שני בנים גדולים ומתו שניהם ביום אחד וקבל עליהם תנחומין ואף אתה
קבל תנחומין. א"ל לא די לי שאני מצטער בעצמי אלא שהזכרתני צערו של אהרן.

נכנס ר"ש וא"ל רבי רצונך אומר דבר אחד לפניך א"ל אמור. א"ל דוד המלך היה
לו בן ומת וקבל עליו תנחומין ואף אתה קבל תנחומין אף אתה רבי קבל תנחומין. א"ל
לא די לי שאני מצטער בעצמי אלא שהזכרתני צערו של דוד המלך.

נכנס ר"א ר' עזריה כיון שראהו אמר לשמשו טול לפני כלי וילך אחרי לבית המרחץ
לפי שאדם גדול הוא ואיני יכול לעמוד בו נכנס וישב לפניו ואמר לו אמשול לך משל
למה"ד לאדם שהפקיד אצלו המלך פקדון בכל יום ויום היה בוכה וצועק ואומר אוי לי
אימתי אצא מן הפקדון הזה בשלום אף אתה רבי היה לך בן קרא תורה מקרא נביאים
וכתובים משנה הלכות ואגדות ונפטר מן העולם בלא חטא ויש לך לקבל עליך תנחומים
כשהחזרת פקדונך שלם א"ל ר' אלעזר בני נחמתני כדרך שבני אדם מנחמין.

The students of Rabbi Yochanan ben Zakkai came to console him
upon the loss of his son. First came Rabbi Eliezer, who pointed out
that although Adam HaRishon had lost a son, Hevel, he accepted
consolation. Rabbi Yochanan ben Zakkai was not consoled. Other
students (Rabbi Yehoshua, Rabbi Yose, and Rabbi Shimon) followed
and referred to others mentioned in *Tanach* (Iyov, Aharon, Dovid
HaMelech) who were consoled despite their tragic personal losses.
The students' message was, ''Rebbi, you should also accept consolation and be comforted.'' But Rabbi Yochanan ben Zakkai remained
grief-stricken. He said, ''Don't I have enough troubles of my own?
Now must I recall and have anguish due to the troubles of Adam
HaRishon, Iyov, Aharon and Dovid HaMelech as well?''

What was wrong with their message? Why was this approach
counter-productive? Why was Rabbi Yochanan ben Zakkai not comforted? Think for a moment. The *choleh* is already hypersensitive to
grief and suffering due to his own situation. He understands only too
well the anguish his family must endure because of it. Hearing about

other misfortunes only adds to his own burden. The visitor doesn't realize this, because he cannot fully internalize the pain of sick people as the *choleh* does.

The manner in which Rabbi Yochanan ben Zakkai is finally comforted is also very instructive.

Rabbi Elazar ben Azariah came to console him and related a story in which a king gives one of his subjects a possession to safeguard. Day and night the man worries, lest something happen to the object. He is greatly relieved when the king eventually reclaims it. Rabbi Elazar ben Azariah concluded, "Rabbi Yochanan, your son, too, was a possession of the King. You raised him and taught him Torah. When the King reclaimed him, he was still as pure as when you first received him." Upon hearing this, Rabbi Yochanan was consoled.

The allegory reminded Rabbi Yochanan ben Zakkai of his purpose in life, and reiterated the positives that existed. It enabled him to focus on better times and connected him to positive images.

❧ Keeping the Connection

Often the *choleh* — cut off from his job, friends, family and responsibilities — loses connection with his life purposes. He suffers from a sense of helplessness and isolation. The *choleh* says, "Look at what has become of me. I have no idea what is happening out there beyond my hospital bed. What's going on at work? At home? With the family? I can't help out no matter how much I want to." This understandably leads to intense feelings of low self-worth.

Many visitors are hesitant to discuss business and work with the *choleh* on the assumption that these discussions will depress him. On the contrary, speaking of these matters is most beneficial and therapeutic. It is helpful if the visitor can pinpoint and elaborate on the *choleh*'s past accomplishments, and reconnect him to what he was doing before the illness began. For example, business associates should discuss the business and what is happening in the office. Neighbors should speak about local events. Family members should keep him up-to-date regarding domestic issues, everyday occurrences, and even simple *narishkeit* (chitchat). Shul members can share the latest shul news (not *lashon hara*). Such discussions are not a burden; rather, they keep the *choleh* connected to his former life, and involved in the world around him. They serve to prevent the *choleh* from slipping into deeper feelings of isolation.

Just prior to being stricken, I had sent my good friend Rabbi Shimshon Sherer a draft of my then upcoming *Shabbos Shuvah derashah* for feedback, as I often do. As I was lying on a gurney waiting for the attendant to take me for additional tests, Rabbi Sherer came running up to visit with me. He told me how much he liked the way I had worked a story about Rabbi Akiva Eiger and the Nesivos into the *derashah*. Right there he asked me to repeat the story to him, and suggested that I call him later for other suggestions. We asked the attendant who was transporting me to stop, and with elevator doors open, I repeated the story. I vividly recall thinking, as the elevator descended, "He really believes that I will be giving that *derashah*! He really believes that I will be able to resume my former life." I have tremendous *chizuk* from that conversation to this very day.

◄§ Look for the Sweetness

L et us consider the situation of a *choleh* who is worried. After all, his own future may be uncertain, and he is anxious about how his family's needs will be met now that he is no longer such a strong presence. A myriad of worries pile up in his mind, and combine with his feeling of powerlessness. What comfort can the visitor offer such a patient who is overwhelmed in this way? In this case, the best approach is to focus on some positive in the *choleh*'s life, despite his admittedly difficult circumstances.

Even in a tragedy, some sweetness can always be found. Hagaon

Harav Gamliel Rabinovitch, *shlita,* of Yerushalayim explained this to me. In the time period when Yosef was sold by his brothers, caravans most often carried merchandise, such as tar or kerosene, that had a very foul odor. Hashem arranged, however, that the caravan transporting Yosef would smell sweet, because it carried *besamim,* aromatic spices. Hashem performed this miracle especially for Yosef, so that he should not suffer from the usual rank odors. Do you really suppose that at the time Yosef's brothers sold him into slavery, he would sit back on the camel and say, "Look how fortunate I am that this caravan is carrying fragrant spices?" What message did Hashem wish to give Yosef (and us)? The lesson is that as painful as this situation was for Yosef, there was still something positive to be appreciated in the event. In every tragedy there will always be a bit of sweetness; our mission is to seek out and find the *besamim* in our situation.

A *choleh* will benefit greatly if a visitor can help him find some "sweetness" in his present situation. Point out good things that remain in his life. For example, a visitor might say, "You must be so proud to see how your family has risen to the occasion." "Look what your friends have done for you." "What a tribute to you that they care so much that they have done even this." I remember clearly that when my own family and friends spoke to me about the positives in my own life, my *hakaras hatov* to Hashem came back into focus. This gave me the strength to handle my difficulties.

In my own situation, I easily found so much *besamim* — sweetness. The incredible strength and faith of my wife and children in the most trying times would have been enough to bolster me. Hearing how my children were learning in yeshivah with such devotion, as if nothing out of the ordinary was going on in their lives, gave me even more strength. But the ultimate sweetness was the *zechus* of marrying off my children to wonderful spouses and having the ability to enjoy the *nachas* of my youngest child Zev Dov's bar mitzvah. Against all odds and against the doctors' predictions, I left my hospital bed in Mount Sinai Hospital and was able to walk (on my own two feet!) my daughter down the aisle to the *chuppah.*

৺ Be There

Another important way to be helpful is to allow the *choleh* to share his feelings and concerns with you. Try to create an atmosphere where the *choleh* feels that his conversation is really welcome. Set aside your preconceived notions of what the visit should be. You don't need to chatter constantly. Be accessible and be a good listener. Just be fully there. Simply give the *choleh* the freedom to say what is on his mind.

There is a discussion in *Maseches Yoma* (75a) between Rav Ami and Rav Assi regarding the verse found in *Mishlei* (12:25): If you have anxiety in your heart, *"yash'chena.'* The Ralbag in *Mishlei* explains that one sage held that *yash'chena* means that the way to deal with worry is to try to quash it and attempt to forget it. There are definitely times when the *choleh* just needs to forget where he is and what is happening to him. I was fortunate to have good friends who repeatedly helped me forget my situation completely. One very memorable occasion was a *simchas bais hasho'eivah* that was held in the *succah* at Mount Sinai Hospital. Friends brought food, music and entertainers to the hospital *succah,* and for those few hours I was no longer a patient in a hospital bed, but once again, a full participant in life.

[Editor's note: I was present, and indeed, this was one of the most unique occasions I have ever had the pleasure of participating in.]

The other sage opined that the way to deal with worry is *yesi'chena* — talk it out. The act of speaking with others and sharing one's thoughts with them lightens a *choleh*'s burden. And it isn't only speaking directly about the person's pain or illness. There are other ways that pain can be eased. When I was first taken to Sloan-Kettering

Medical Center, a good friend went to get a *berachah* for me from Hagaon Harav Chaim Kanievsky, *shlita*. The Rav gave a *berachah* and said that at the first sign of any improvement in my condition, a *minyan* of people should gather together and recite the *tefillah* of *Nishmas*.

As soon as we saw some slight improvement, a good friend of mine came to the hospital. He said, "Simcha, give me your hand." I could barely move some parts of my body, but I managed to move the hand somewhat. He grabbed it and pulled me out of bed, and with the help of several others, he got me into a stretcher chair. They proceeded to wheel me downstairs to the chapel at Sloan-Kettering where there is a *minyan* for *Minchah* every day. The *minyan* is comprised mainly of the very busy religious doctors who practice there. At the conclusion of *Minchah,* my friend made an announcement that we would then all say *Nishmas* out loud together. None of the others asked why we would be saying *Nishmas* in the middle of the weekday *Minchah,* and nobody said he was in a rush. They all stayed to participate in the *tefillah* for my sake and said *Nishmas* like never before, with huge *kavannah*.

This beautiful moment shows that *yash'chena* can be brought about by sharing actions together, as well as by conventional discussions. Through these lively "golden moments," a *mevaker* can bring delight and *simchah* to the *choleh* that touch him to the core.

Part of genuine sensitivity to a *choleh*'s feelings is knowing when he does *not* want to talk things over. Sometimes there are good reasons for being quiet. The *Sefer Chassidim* (627) analyzes this verse: "The heart knows the bitterness of the soul" (*Mishlei* 14:10). The author asks: Since the heart knows the soul's bitterness, why state the obvious? The verse teaches us that there are times when one should keep his pain in his heart, and not share it with others. When should that be? The *choleh* knows when his visitor is not truly concerned with his problems. If he senses that the visitor does not want to hear about his feelings, he will certainly keep them to himself. The visitor needs to be honest with himself, as well as with the *choleh*. The realities, the truths of our relationships with each other are present, even in the hospital room. A visit is helpful only if it is derived from sincere caring.

◄§ Strengthening the Choleh

A s I go forward with my life, one thought gives me support as I use my experiences to help others cope with their painful circumstances. At the worst point of my illness, I was immobilized and confined to my hospital bed. I was totally dependant on nurses and aides to assist me with my most private needs. My feeling of helplessness was intensified by feelings of humiliation and indignity at needing to be helped in this way. I knew then that this aspect was not going to get better quickly, and that I needed to find some thought, some idea, to help me get through it. Then, one day, a song popped into my head and I found it to be a powerful source of encouragement and resolve. I began to sing:

אשרנו מה טוב חלקנו ומה נעים גורלנו ומה יפה ירושתינו — *How fortunate are we and how good is our lot. And how sweet is our portion and how beautiful is our heritage.*

Thinking of this song reaffirmed for me the idea that no matter where we are, and no matter what shape we are in physically, we are still very special. We all are imbued with a soul that is a piece of Hashem and we are all created in His image. That didn't change when I became sick, and that part of me is healthy, well and whole, and will eternally be so. *Nobody can take that away from me — ever!* That singular thought has sustained me through all of my trials and tribulations. It is something I try to impart to others as well. For the *choleh* who is at rock-bottom and in despair, being reminded that he is part of Hashem and that he is made in His image is transformative. At the end of the day, it is something that nothing and no one can take away from him, despite his very real suffering.

What then, have I learned about the mitzvah of bikur cholim from my experience of needing it and then receiving it in such abundance?

I would say that the *chesed* in the heart of the visitor makes more of an impact than he can realize. The *choleh*'s life as he once knew it has been taken away from him. He is given the challenge of maintaining his completeness and his sense of self under new and trying circumstances. This self-reconstruction is a fragile process, and well-wishers play a vital role in strengthening him as he struggles with that process.

The key, after all, is that bikur cholim and expressing the *berachah* for a *refuah sheleimah* are not simply words spoken between people in a random way. The mitzvah of bikur cholim, in the context of our community's observance of mitzvos, is Hashem's way of bringing His caring and encouragement to each *choleh*. It's more than just words. Each visit, each get-well card, each phone call and each small gift carries a message from Hashem. If we can learn to put a little more thought into how we express our good wishes, if we can tune in a little more accurately to the feelings of the *choleh*, perhaps *HaKadosh Baruch Hu's* "messages" will come through more clearly.

I know that I have grown and learned a great deal through this process — in ways that I would not and could not under "normal" circumstances. The merit for all of this is due to all of those who came to my side during those hard times. Yasheir Koach.

IT'S ALL ABOUT THE CHOLEH

Rabbi Mordechai Kamenetzky
Rosh Yeshivah, Yeshivah of South Shore,
Hewlett, NY

Bikur cholim is as old as illness itself. It is considered one of the premier forms of *chesed* that humans can perform. The goal of mankind is to emulate the Creator. One of the earliest and most evident acts of the Almighty's kindness was manifest in His visiting the sick. The first recorded act of visiting the sick was none other than the Almighty Who, according to *Chazal*, visited Avraham on the third day after his *bris milah.*

That inimitable visit surely sets a standard of bikur cholim that we, as hard as we may try, can never replicate; yet from that very visit there is much to learn — even in a practical sense — and apply to our own visits to the sick.

The Midrash tells us that Hashem had removed the sun from its casing in order to dissuade wayfarers from traveling and thus burdening Avraham Avinu. It is therefore perplexing that Hashem chose to have His designated visitors, the angelic messengers, appear precisely while He was conferring with Avraham. These angels were His messengers. Why didn't the *Ribbono Shel Olam* instruct them to wait until after His conversation with Avraham had been concluded? Why did Hashem set up what seems to be a conflict of interest where Avraham had to choose between nomads and God? Indeed it was a choice that resulted in the Almighty's deferral to those who appeared to be from the lowest, most common examples of His human creation.

And though Avraham's choice set an eternal precedent for his

This chapter was written by a noted *talmid chacham,* a popular and prolific author who needs no introduction. He is writing from the perspective of a parent who experienced serious illness in the family. May Hashem continue to bestow His *berachah* upon the family.

descendants — that welcoming guests takes precedence over greeting the *Shechinah* — I was always bothered as to why that incident had to transpire during the course of a visit to someone who was ill.

Couldn't one of the myriad instances of Avraham's greeting a guest been the impetus for the "guest vs. *Shechinah*" preference.

When visiting a person who is ill, there is an interaction between (at least) two individuals. There are the patient's needs and there are the visitor's needs. There are countless interactions and occurrences during a patient's stay in a hospital or even while convalescing at home or in a health care facility. There are tests, procedures, nurses and doctors. There may be an important phone call for which a patient or his family have been waiting. The world of the *choleh* is not placed on hold during your visit. We must not lose focus of the fact that the visit is not about the visitor's needs, it is about the *choleh's* needs.

Perhaps Hashem set the precedent in coming to visit Avraham and then deferring to what was Avraham's desire. The *Ribbono Shel Olam* set a precedent to teach that the visit is not about the visitor. It's about the *choleh*. And the *choleh's* needs — whether they are seemingly irre-levant, a frivolous wish, or a desire to confer with a renowned specialist — take precedence over the visitor's needs for the moment.

◄§ The Visit

As enthusiastic as one may be in wanting to visit someone who is sick, and as well-intentioned as one may be, a visit to a hospital, nursing home, or even someone's home requires careful deliberation and preparation.

Of course these preparations must take into consideration the severity of the illness and the state of mind of the patient and family. Do they want visitors? Some people are not as ready to receive, as much as others are ready to visit. Firstly, a phone call is invariably in order. If you can't speak to the one who is ill, contact a caregiver to find out if it is an appropriate time to visit. Often there are tests and procedures that preclude visits and limit the patient's interaction with visitors. This makes both parties uncomfortable. Is it a good time to visit? Does the patient need something that you can bring? Will your visit benefit the *choleh* or is it just the fulfillment of your mitzvah obligation and social responsibility?

Be aware of your own presence and situation as well. The fact that your nagging cold did not deter you from putting in a full day at the office does not mean it should not deter you from visiting the sick. You may have the strength and fortitude, but remember, you also have the germs. Stay home.

A visitor can sometimes be the necessary conduit to the outside world. For better or for worse, word may not have spread that someone is ill. There are those patients who want privacy while others want visitors — even a commotion and effervescent atmosphere. If you pay close attention you should be able to recognize the patient's needs and desires and aid him or her in getting the message out in the proper manner to the ideal parties.

Try to make the patient feel in control. A patient in a hospital is deprived of so much privacy, and often dignity. Treating the hospital room like a private domain gives the sense of dignity. Knock before entering a room and when a curtain is drawn don't move it without permission.

When you enter be cheerful and don't add to the patient's problems. You can discuss the various cards and gifts in the room and try to focus on things that bring *nachas* and joy.

Never criticize the hospital, the doctors, the food, or the medical procedures. Criticizing a patient's care may diminish his or her confidence in the prescribed treatment plan. If the patient is frustrated with the care he or she is receiving, listen sympathetically without necessarily agreeing.

Time your visit properly. People occasionally visit a patient on the way to a wedding or other *simchah*. They are dressed in their finest clothes and jewelry. They come and go quickly after describing (albeit not maliciously) the wonderful time that they are about to have. Though their visit was intended as an act of *chesed*, the patient may feel that it was just a quick pit stop on the way to elsewhere. While visiting, try to relax and not give the impression that every moment with the patient is spent on *shpilkes,* in order to be able to say, "we visited." Indeed, in most instances, one should not stay long, but to make it clear that the visit is merely an interruption of an otherwise glamorous evening is insensitive and clearly not beneficial. After the visit, the patient is left with the images of the adorned wife's jewels still glittering in his eyes, the aromas of the smorgasbord wafting in the air, and the strains of the music playing in his mind.

When a couple visits and only one of the pair knows the *choleh*, the other party may feel and act uncomfortable. Cell phones are prohibited in many hospitals, but work despite the ban. Their use in front of patients and, even more so, a subsequent chiding by a nurse or other practitioner will embarrass the patient and the People of the Book. Simply put it's a *chillul Hashem*; obey the hospital rules.

Don't be afraid to sit quietly. You don't have to say anything. Remember, the main reason of the visit is to bring comfort and friendship and to show concern. Your presence speaks louder than words.

Listen. Besides demonstrating your concern with your physical presence, you can also do so by allowing the patient to voice his concerns. In fact, this is a major service one can offer. If people who are sick wish to speak about their illness — or about anything else — then listen. All of us have a need to be heard, most of all when we are stressed or ill.

Hospital rooms can become gathering places. Your primary job is to have the welfare of the patient in mind. Bikur cholim has no other objective. It is **not** the place to meet friends, catch up on the latest gossip or hear about new therapies that are being offered. Likewise, be mindful of the patient's condition and limit your time accordingly.

It is important to spend time with the patient's children or siblings as well and extend appropriate assistance. Seeing that his or her family is attended to during a difficult time can bring significant pleasure and comfort to someone who is ill.

One should also bear in mind that no matter how close he or she may be to the *choleh,* the family's relationship takes precedence. Your visit may infringe on children and grandchildren who are visiting and cannot come often, and who may not be comfortable having you present during their visit. Don't assume that extended family members have the ability to visit whenever they want. They may have flown in from out-of-town for the day, only to have their brief opportunity to be with the patient inappropriately usurped by an outsider's imposition, no matter how well meaning.

◄§ True Concern

Indeed, one of the keys to bikur cholim is to truly be concerned. To exercise compassion and concern, and not merely go through the motions, you must actually feel compassion and concern. That is not an action; it is an emotion. You must feel concern to act concerned. True concern without any injections of self will enable one to act appropriately when visiting the sick. When one is really involved with the total welfare of the *choleh*, he or she is able to speak to the patient without any faux pas that so often occurs.

When the Bluzhever Rebbe was sick, there is a wonderful story told about a particular Rosh Yeshivah who called the Rebbe and informed him that he would like to visit to fulfill the mitzvah of bikur cholim.

The Rebbe jokingly replied, "In the yeshivah world there are always two entities to a mitzvah. There is the *gavrah,* the man who is doing the *mitzvah*, and then there is the *cheftzah* of the mitzvah, the item that is being used to perform the mitzvah, e.g., a man shaking a *lulav*, a woman separating *challah*. With all due respect, I would like to remain a *gavrah*, and not your *cheftzah shel mitzvah!*"

Clearly we mustn't make the *choleh* our vehicle on the road to mitzvah performance. In fact, if the patient is sleeping and we visit and do not wake him up, we have fulfilled the mitzvah. The patient does not know that we visited. He or she never saw us. Yet we did the mitzvah. It is not about interaction or bragging rights. It is about concern. It is about asking Hashem for a *refuah sheleimah*.

⨾ Do You Really Know?

Often people visit the sick and begin their visit with the words, "I know what you are going through." Do you? You may have had a broken leg, as does the patient, but was yours shattered in three places. Was it a week before your daughter's wedding? Every situation is different.

Each medical situation is unique and produces totally different results, feelings and emotions. The same disease may have resulted in diverse prognoses. Age and prior medical history are factors in the variants, as well as family and financial support. So even if you think you know what someone is going through, you probably don't.

If you are a survivor or the caregiver of a survivor, sharing specific stories of similar experiences can be helpful if they show how you were able to overcome particular situations and if there was a positive outcome.

A young mother with a large family told me of how, shortly after giving birth to a baby, her oldest son was diagnosed with a life-threatening illness. Following the initial diagnosis, a social worker came in the room and with a dour look of despair sadly remarked, "You must really have your hands full."

The mother smiled as if to say, "Lady, I don't know about you, but I can handle this okay. Don't tell me that I cannot."

Indeed, everyone reacts differently to illness. Because you may have felt it was important to talk about your illness, it does not mean that your ill friend has to talk about it. Even within a family, there are different ways people deal with crisis and illness. Like my father often says, "Many ships have crossed the ocean, but none have made a path."

In our community, many of us are well versed in medical issues and not uncomfortable in the environs of a hospital. Many of us are not intimidated by ICUs and we feel at ease in the presence of various machines and important doctors. But that familiarity can often lead to asking too many questions, or offering inappropriate suggestions. Be careful. There is a morbid curiosity that many of us have about illness and even death. Illness breeds strange questions: When did the disease begin? What prompted you to visit the doctor? Who is doing the surgery? What type of chemo are you on? Will you lose your hair? What are the side effects of radiation? How long do you have to be laid up? And the worst of all, "So what's the prognosis?"

I often respond to that obtuse question with the following: "What was the prognosis of 3,000 people who worked at the World Trade Center on September 10, '01?"

It is important for patients and parents and family members to keep in mind that people mean well, they just make mistakes. Some have a lot on their minds as well and need someone with whom to share their experiences or emotions. I was told of a man whose son was diagnosed with a particular form of cancer. An old friend from his high school days came to visit shortly after the diagnosis and the notification that chemotherapy would be part of the medical proto- col. The friend began discussing a variety of chemical agents used in treatments that had no bearing on the boy's illness. The mystified father, who was not yet informed about the exact protocol that his son would have to undergo, just nodded in utter confusion as the friend continued with a barrage of what turned out to be useless information.

Almost two years later, the friend met the father of the boy, who was then doing quite well, *baruch Hashem*. The friend explained his bizarre behavior. At that time his own wife had recently been diagnosed and had subsequently survived a totally different form of cancer. "We did not tell anyone at the time, and I needed to vent my emotions. I know it was inappropriate and I apologize."

The father of the young man smiled and responded, "At that point in our crisis I was so overwhelmed that I probably did not digest anything you said. But *Chazal* tell us (regarding prayer): "Whether one does a little, or whether one does a lot — [it is good] as long as one directs his heart, *l'shem Shamayim*, for the sake of Heaven.' As long as you meant well, I'm okay with it."

Patients, parents of patients and family members can often become irritated by the lack of common sense of visitors. But remember, people mean well, even if they act, well — mean.

In order to stem the flow of inane questions, one patient had a list of answers on his hospital room door. It was numbered 1-30. Here are the first ten:

1. Yes
2. No
3. Dr. Cohen
4. Maybe
5. Tomorrow
7. Pizza
8. 4 Weeks
9. Pickles
10. 11:00

and so on. On the bottom was written: "Thank you for your concern. Above are the answers to your questions. They are all there. Please choose the appropriate answer and do not burden the patient or his family."

I do not mean to belittle or insult those who ask questions. It is difficult to draw the line within our own souls between concern and curiosity. Somehow we may feel that the answer to a pertinent question may help us understand the illness and even help us offer a revolutionary cure or piece of advice.

None of these questions are really your concern and should not be discussed unless — of course — the patient offers or asks. And even then, one must use prudence when seeking to be helpful. There is a difference between talking to a patient and to a caregiver. There is a difference between talking to a caregiver privately and talking in front of the patient. Use discretion! Indeed some of us may have very important knowledge to offer, but sometimes a little knowledge is dangerous.

That does not say that you should totally remove yourself from the experience. People who have had similar experiences can lend tremendous encouragement. A person who has gone through the same sort of illness and endured, persevered, and is a living example of Hashem's lovingkindness is always a source of tremendous inspiration to an individual and family going through illness. But be careful to bring along good news. It is of very little value to tell tales of unsuccessful treatments and botched surgeries. This will only serve to discourage the *choleh*. In fact the Torah prohibits bearing news that can aggravate a *choleh*.

The mother of a patient related how an acquaintance called.

"I heard your son was diagnosed with so and so."

After a quiet pause, "Yes."

"Oh I know all about it! My nephew had it!"

The friend went on in a very helpful and informative way to talk about treatments and medicines, displaying her knowledge of the names of many of the specialists in that field.

Finally the sick boy's mother asked. "So, how's your nephew?"

The answer was somewhat matter-of-fact. "Oh, he died a few months ago."

I think no further comment is necessary.

Another issue: Because one has experience with a variant form of one disease does not mean that he is knowledgeable about another form. Suggestions and advice regarding various forms of treatment can cause tremendous anguish to a second-guessed patient or his caregiver. Alternative medicines, herbal potions, and vitamin supplements can be helpful additions to the prescribed treatment; they can also interact in a harmful manner. There are also unconventional cures that many people like to bandy about. The worst is when the so-called advisers make you feel guilty for not leaving your doctor for the herbalist on a reservation in New Mexico whom they heard of thirdhand from a friend who read a *Reader's Digest* in a beauty parlor. Clearly imposing your fund of unconventional wisdom on families or patients is unfair, and making them feel guilty for ignoring your advice is unwarranted — actually it is inexcusable.

(Ed. Note: Indeed, it is my opinion that should these advisers convince a naive patient to forgo or not accept an acknowledged proven medical therapy (*refuah bedukah*), it is akin to being an accomplice to murder).

But the most difficult thing for a patient is to have someone directly second-guess his treatment to his face. If you feel that a change is in order to the extent that you consider it a matter of *pikuach nefesh*, then perhaps you should consult a close relative of the *choleh* or his Rav.

I will never forget how not long after we had chosen a surgeon for a difficult operation, someone who had a reputation as being quite knowledgeable regarding doctors told me, based on a particular singular experience, "Oh, don't use Dr. X. He is a *rotzei'ach*, a murderer." We did not listen and now we regard the surgeon as a savior.

If you feel you have solid information, do not confuse the patient; speak with the individual to whom the family will turn for advice. This person can explore the various avenues of approach. Should the suggested therapy seem as worthless as snake oil, then you will look bad and the *choleh* as well as his loved ones will have been subjected to grueling emotional anguish. Once a course of treatment is decided upon, be supportive and do not persist with your claim that your way will yield certain success.

◆§ Chizuk

I am convinced that even in situations where you cannot visit a sick person there are so many way to be *mechazek* a *choleh* or the family of a *choleh*.

I am not sure if you will fulfill the mitzvah of *bikur cholim* through such actions, but it clearly is a *gemillas chesed* (act of kindness)!

When people meet a *choleh* or a family member and mention that they have been thinking of him, or ask about the *choleh* by the name used in *tefillah* (*Ploni(s) ben or bas Plonis*), it shows that they care enough to remember and that the requests to *daven* really meant something.

I know of a father who went to Eretz Yisrael with his son who was diagnosed with a serious disease. There, in a whirlwind three days, they met many *gedolim* and *tzaddikim* who took the name of the *choleh* (we will call him Chaim Baruch *ben* Rivka Nechamah), offered their *berachos* and gave tremendous *chizuk*.

The father told of two amazing occurrences that almost assured him that miracles were bound to happen. He was approached at the *Kosel* by one of the ubiquitous collectors who seem to accost every American visitor.

As the goal of the trip was to be as gracious in *tzeddakah* as possible, the father pulled out a large bill (many times larger than the standard $5 fare). He offered it to one of the more respectable-looking collectors. Before placing it in the outstretched hand the father of the ill child added, "I am giving this to you but I want you to *daven* for Chaim Baruch ben Rivka . . ." The father did not finish the name. As he pulled out a notebook from his vest, the collector recited the name of the *choleh*. As he mentioned the name, the collector showed the father the notebook. There, scrawled on the first page, in bold letters atop a list of names was written: "Please *daven* for Chaim Baruch *ben* Rivka Nechamah. The father could not believe what he saw. This stranger had his son's name front and center in his "prayer book"!

That display of concern was worth double the intended donation. And indeed the man received double the intended donation.

Another stop was the Rosh Yeshivah of Yeshivas Eitz Chaim, Rav Ephraim Zalaznick.

The visit was brief but meaningful, but the greatest *chizuk* came six months later, when a friend of the young man, who was then in yeshivah in Israel, related to him, "Chaim Baruch! You are not going to believe this! I was in Eretz Yisrael last week and I went to speak to Rav Ephraim Zalaznick. He was in the middle of learning and believe it or not right on top of the *amud* Gemara he was learning there was a piece of paper with your name! Indeed, written in bold letters I saw the name, Chaim Baruch *ben* Rivka Nechamah!

The *chizuk* was derived from both the Rosh Yeshivah and the one who related the story.

You may receive an array of books, pamphlets and leaflets each expressing ways to strengthen a particular mitzvah. Many have the name of a *choleh* at the bottom. It is difficult to comprehend the *chizuk* received by the *choleh* or his family when they receive a call stating how useful the book is.

(After asking our family's permission), in zechus of a *refuah sheleimah* for our son, a friend sent out an illuminated *Al Ha-Michyah* to a group of our friends in Woodmere. One of the most heartwarming calls we received in response to the mailing came from a woman who called admitting that this was the first time she really said *Al haMichyah* in her entire life. All for the intended *zechus* of the *choleh*.

If you let people know that they are on your mind, you have become part of their lives.

I recently attended a wedding where I met the Bluzhever Rebbe. I introduced myself to the Rebbe as Mordechai Kamenetzky. He asked me if I was a grandson of Rav Yaakov Kamenetzky *zt"l* and if I was related to Rav Binyamin Kamenetzky, *shlita*. I affirmed that indeed I was a grandson of Rav Yaakov and a son of Rav Binyamin.

"I am so happy I met you," he exclaimed. "Almost 5 years ago, I met your father and he asked me to *daven* for a grandson who was diagnosed with a serious illness. I did not have his number and I have not heard or seen him since and I have not stopped davening. "Do you know who I am talking about? How is the boy doing? Please let me know."

I was shocked. Five years ago? I answered in awe, "Yes, Rebbe, I do know. You are davening for *my* son and *baruch Hashem* he is doing very well. He is *baruch Hashem* married to a wonderful girl and in fact they are expecting a baby very soon."

That incident demonstrates what true concern means.

A simple but great act of *chizuk* that one can do, beyond a phone call, is to write a letter or even a note. A letter of encouragement shows that you truly care. It shows that you took the time to gather your thoughts and express deep concern. Making a tape especially for teen peers is wonderful. The friends can be really imaginative and can enable their laid-up friend to feel part of the *chevrah* (group). Indeed a visit is always appreciated, but sometimes a fleeting stop in the hospital may not be as meaningful as a creative and lasting form of *chizuk* that shows true care and concern. There are feelings of faith and *bitachon* that one can express in a letter that are difficult to articulate in person. And a letter can be read over and over again.

Sickness passes. We all hope that it passes with healing and not with a passing away. But a visit and its ramifications endure forever with a patient and his or her loved ones. Take great care to make sure that your visit, or whatever you do to encourage the *choleh*, is uplifting, heartening and meaningful. Remember — it is part of the cure.

Selected Responsa from Igros Moshe Yechaveh Daas Tzitz Eliezer

Adaptations of selected responsa dealing with practical issues of bikur cholim.

SELECTED RESPONSA FROM IGROS MOSHE
(R' Moshe Feinstein זצ"ל)

∼§ Yoreh De'ah 1:223

- One is obligated to visit the sick individual in person.
- One incapable of actually going to visit the sick person should at least telephone.
- *Tefillos* recited at the bedside have unique value — even if others will *daven* there.

Regarding fulfilling the mitzvah of bikur cholim via a telephone call, HaRav Moshe Feinstein writes that in a situation where one is unable to actually visit the person, one should at least telephone and try as much as possible to fulfill the mitzvah in this fashion. However, when one can pay a visit, one should not free himself of this obligation or be satisfied with just a telephone call. Indeed, if one can do so, one is obligated to visit the sick individual in person because this will provide him with much greater comfort. In addition, the visitor will have a better grasp of the sick person's plight and therefore will *daven* more effectively on his behalf. Furthermore, the *tefillos* will be more fully accepted at the sick person's bedside, because that is where the *Shechinah* is found. However, if one is unable to visit, or if the sick person is unable to accept visitors, then one should certainly strive to at least fulfill the mitzvah via telephone. HaRav Moshe adds that when you visit a sick person, your *tefillos* at the bedside have unique value — even if others will *daven* there. This is because every single person who *davens* is providing additional benefit to the *choleh*. Furthermore, HaRav Moshe adds that even though you may hear about how severely ill the person is, seeing this with your own eyes will heighten your emotions — and your prayers — on the sick person's behalf.

- A prestigious person is obligated to visit people who are ill even if they are younger than he is.
- This visitation does not compromise nor lessen the status of the more respected person.
- A sick person's pain and suffering take precedence over a *talmid chacham*'s potential loss of honor.

In this *teshuvah,* HaRav Moshe Feinstein clarifies why an older, more prestigious person is obligated to visit a younger person who is ill. Addressing the *Shalmei Nedarim's* questions — "Why is an older, more respected person obligated to visit a younger person who is ill? Doesn't this compromise the respect that is due a *talmid chacham?*" — HaRav Moshe begins by acknowledging that it does not suffice to assert that traveling to visit the sick does not compromise the older person's *kavod*; in truth, traveling is beneath his dignity and does compromise the respect that is due him as required by the Torah.

Likewise, HaRav Moshe continues, one cannot argue that an observer would realize that a *talmid chacham* who visits the sick is fulfilling Hashem's will and that therefore his *kavod* has not been compromised. After all, the Torah does not obligate a person to be more careful with his neighbor's money than with his own; hence, he is not obligated to pick up and return an object if it is beneath his dignity to do so, as long as he would not pick it up even for himself. Similarly, an older person does not have to testify in court regarding another's monetary matter if, considering it beneath his dignity, he would not do so for himself. Hence, even though he is performing a mitzvah, this does not automatically negate a concern for a *talmid chacham*'s dignity.

HaRav Moshe's ruling would apply to all *bein adam l'chaveiro* (between man and his fellow) obligations, including visiting the sick. If a *talmid chacham* would not visit a sick person in his own family, he would not be obligated to visit a non-relative of the same stature.

Therefore, this is not an acceptable explanation for why a prestigious person must go and visit a less prestigious one.

A third hypothesis proffered — and rejected — by HaRav Moshe is that bikur cholim is a matter of life and death, overriding the requirement to honor a *talmid chacham*. HaRav Moshe rejects this hypothesis because the mitzvah of bikur cholim applies even when the *choleh* does not have a life-threatening illness. This is proven from the fact that visiting a house of *shivah* to comfort a mourner takes precedence over the mitzvah of bikur cholim. However, if indeed we were referring only to bikur cholim on behalf of someone with a life-threatening illness, then the mitzvah of visiting the mourners would not take precedence over that of visiting the sick, as it would be pushed aside by the precept that saving a life takes precedence over all mitzvos (except transgressing the three Cardinal Sins: illicit relations, idol worship and murder).

Therefore, the answer to the *Shalmei Nedarim's* question — "Why is a prestigious person, a *talmid chacham*, obligated to visit a less prestigious person?" — is based upon the following principle: One's personal dignity and honor do not take precedence over another person's suffering. A sick person's pain and suffering — even when not life-threatening — take precedence over the *talmid chacham's* potential loss of honor. This is the conclusion HaRav Moshe reached — that a greater person must go and visit a less prestigious person.

◆§ Yoreh De'ah 1:223

- One partially fulfills bikur cholim via a telephone call.
- One who cannot visit is still obligated to perform those aspects of bikur cholim activities that do not require one's physical presence.

In this *teshuvah*, HaRav Moshe discusses further the concept of bikur cholim via telephone. He had been asked: Even if a person does not perform every component of bikur cholim brought down in the name of the Ramban by the *Tur* and the *Beis Yosef* in *Siman* 335, can he nevertheless be considered to have fulfilled the mitzvah of bikur cholim if he performed at least one of these component parts? HaRav Moshe responds that, in his humble opinion, it is obvious that the person has fulfilled part of the mitzvah of bikur cholim, but one certainly cannot say that he has fulfilled all of his obligations regarding bikur cholim, since he did not perform all of its component parts. If he placed the telephone call because he was unable to physically go and visit the sick person, at least he did what he could. Under these circumstances, since he was unable to visit, he is not liable.

However, one cannot presume to be released from his obligation even if the choleh does not want visitors. In addition, one has not fully discharged his responsibility of visiting the sick simply by taking care of their needs from a distance or by asking how they are faring if one is physically able to pay a visit. Even if one cannot visit, one is not exempt from doing the things that do not require one's physical presence. Indeed, HaRav Moshe says that one is obligated to visit cholim because the visit will bring them comfort that cannot be duplicated in any other fashion. Furthermore, seeing the patient will spur the visitor to pray more intensely on his behalf; descriptions provided by other visitors will in no way elicit the same kavannah. In fact, one's prayers have a better chance of being accepted in the sick person's presence because the Shechinah's Presence is felt more closely there. HaRav Moshe concludes that one certainly must do everything possible to visit the sick in person, but when one is unable to do so, a telephone call will fulfill some components of the mitzvah of bikur cholim.

◀§ Yoreh De'ah 1:223

- A paid agent is credited with fulfilling the mitzvah of bikur cholim, as is the person who sent him.

HaRav Moshe Feinstein discusses whether a paid agent is credited with fulfilling the mitzvah of bikur cholim. He asserts that the agent clearly fulfills the mitzvah. Furthermore, the person who sent him partially fulfills the mitzvah by having spent money for the choleh's benefit.

- One is obligated to pray for the sick.
- Prayers and blessings of each and every person are beneficial.
- Praying — unlike caregiving — is a mitzvah that cannot be delegated.

HaRav Moshe Feinstein writes that the essential component of bikur cholim, based upon the Gemara (*Shabbos* 12b and *Nedarim* 40a), is praying that Hashem grant the sick person a *refuah*. He adds that bikur cholim is a mitzvah and an obligation upon every member of Klal Yisrael, even average people whose *tefillos* might not be accepted by Hashem. One is therefore forced to conclude that the prayers and blessings of every single person — even average people, even people who do not meticulously avoid sin — are beneficial. This is true even when they visit a *choleh* by themselves; there certainly is no obligation to visit a *choleh* as part of a *minyan* of visitors. In fact, unless the *choleh*'s doctor specifically permits it, it is generally prohibited for a large group to visit a *choleh* at one time. Therefore, one must conclude that Hashem indeed desires and accepts the prayers of every single individual, even one who is average or who has sinned, and is not concerned about having sinned. Even this person's prayers matter, and he should go and visit the sick.

However, HaRav Moshe points out (*Igros Moshe, Yoreh De'ah* 1:223) that other aspects of bikur cholim (cleaning, washing and otherwise taking care of the *choleh*) are also extremely important. The difference between praying and caring for the *choleh* is that praying — unlike caregiving — is a mitzvah that cannot be delegated. Even if others are praying for the *choleh*, one should pray as well because the more people who pray the better, since the prayers are cumulative; and unlike caregiving, which once done is no longer necessary, each prayer has its own value. Similarly, the *Tzitz Eliezer* (*Chelek* 17, *Siman* 6) mentions the famous story recounted in the Gemara (*Berachos* 10a) of how Chizkiyahu HaMelech and

Yeshayahu HaNavi did not visit one another. [Ed. note: This was based upon a halachic disagreement over whether it was incumbent upon the prophet to visit the king, or vice versa.] Therefore, Hashem made Chizkiyahu ill and Yeshayahu had to visit him because of the obligation of bikur cholim. We see here a clear proof that one must personally visit the sick and not send a messenger, because if the sole purpose of Yeshayahu's visit to Chizkiyahu was, as the Gemara describes, to tell the king that he was going to die since he had neglected the mitzvah to marry, Yeshayahu could have accomplished this via a messenger. We learn from the fact that the prophet himself paid this visit that there is a personal obligation to visit the sick instead of delegating a messenger.

⇥ Yoreh De'ah 2:166

- In cases of great need, a Kohen is permitted to visit a hospitalized *choleh*.

HaRav Moshe Feinstein was presented with the question: Can a Kohen visit a *choleh* in a hospital? The issue revolves around the high probability that there will be corpse *tumah* (ritual impurity) in the hospital that will be transmitted to a Kohen who enters that building. In addition to the possibility of a corpse in the building, body parts that have been amputated or removed from patients may be in the hospital, and they too transmit such *tumah*. However, HaRav Moshe writes that since most patients in U.S. hospitals are non-Jews, and since — in neighborhoods where there are significant numbers of Jews — the majority of Jews refuse to authorize autopsies, there is a halachic presumption that any corpse or body part in the hospital does not belong to a Jew and therefore cannot transmit corpse *tumah* to a person under the same roof. [Ed. note: However, the corpse of a non-Jew does transmit *tumah* by contact or by carrying.] Therefore, in cases of great need (for example, to visit a sick relative [such as one's father or son], or even one's wife's relatives [to promote *shalom bayis*, harmony in the home], and certainly one's wife [which is the paradigmatic example of promoting *shalom bayis*]), a Kohen is permitted to visit a hospitalized *choleh*. However, the Kohen should make a diligent effort to determine if indeed there is a Jewish corpse in the building. [Ed. note: In various Israeli hospitals, to prevent *tumah* concerns special signs and lights indicate if there is a Jewish corpse in the building so that Kohanim will not enter or, if they are already inside, will leave via the nearest exit.] HaRav Moshe adds that if a Kohen cannot ascertain whether or not there is a Jewish corpse in the hospital, he can still rely upon the presumption that there is no such *tumah* present and proceed with his visit. [Ed. note: One can surmise that HaRav Moshe would not favor Kohanim routinely visiting non-relatives in hospitals, but he certainly would encourage them to visit *cholim* in their homes, where there is no concern of corpse *tumah*.]

⋖ Orach Chaim 4; 40:11

- Comforting mourners takes precedence over visiting the sick if the needs of the sick are being taken care of.

HaRav Moshe Feinstein also addresses the Rambam, who states that *nichum aveilim* (comforting mourners) takes precedence over bikur cholim. He writes that the Rambam clearly is referring to a situation in which the *choleh*'s needs are being met, because if this were not true, even though *nichum aveilim* incorporates *chesed* for both the living and the dead, one would be obligated to take care of the *choleh* because *pikuach nefesh* (saving a life) supersedes all other mitzvos. Even *talmud Torah* (for oneself or for the public), which Rav Yosef (*Megillah* 16) asserts is — in theory — of more importance than saving lives, must be put aside in order to actually save even one life in Israel. Therefore, the Rambam's intention is just to show that — regarding the importance of the mitzvos in and of themselves — comforting mourners takes precedence over visiting the sick because of the twofold imperative of *chesed* to the living and to the dead, *only* when there is no possibility of *pikuach nefesh* (life-threatening danger) for the *choleh* (in other words, when all of the *choleh*'s needs are being met).

HaRav Moshe then cites the *Radvaz*, who suggests that since there may be an aspect of *pikuach nefesh* in every case of bikur cholim, that mitzvah should always take precedence over comforting mourners. In other words, if one were to visit mourners before visiting the sick, this might lead in some situations to a loss of life; therefore, one should always visit the sick before visiting mourners. HaRav Moshe interprets the *Radvaz* as saying that even when one is certain that all the *choleh*'s needs are being met, bikur cholim takes precedence over comforting mourners because of one's ability to pray at the *choleh*'s bedside. This, HaRav Moshe says, is the point of contention in the Rambam, who differs with this *Radvaz*: Since one can pray even when one is not at the *choleh*'s bedside, the twofold *chesed* to both the living and the dead (accomplished when comforting mourners) overrides the single act of *chesed* toward the living that is accomplished when visiting the sick. HaRav Moshe therefore rules that when there is absolutely no doubt that the needs of the *choleh* are being met, visiting and comforting a mourner take precedence over visiting the sick.

A RESPONSA FROM YECHAVEH DAAS

(R' Ovadia Yossef שליט"א)

✑ Chelek 3, Siman 83

- One who has the ability to visit the *choleh* does not fulfill the mitzvah fully via a telephone call or a letter.
- *Tefillos* in the presence of the sick person are more likely to be accepted.

When asked: "Can one fulfill the obligation of bikur cholim by inquiring via telephone about the sick person's well-being and wishing that person a *refuah sheleimah*, or must one visit at the *choleh*'s bedside?," the Yechaveh Daas replied that if one has the ability to visit the *choleh*, one does not fulfill the mitzvah fully via a telephone call or a letter. However, praying for Hashem's merciful intervention can be done even when one is not in front of the *choleh* (e.g., by making a *mi shebeirach* as part of a *minyan* in shul, since the *Shechinah* always dwells where a *minyan* is present). However, *tefillos* in front of the sick person are more likely to be accepted. The Yechaveh Daas also cites an *Ein Yaakov* (from *Berachos* 34a) that states that one need not mention the *choleh*'s name when in his presence and that, in fact, mentioning the name may cause harm because the name may have caused (or been a factor in) that person's illness. Similarly, we sometimes change a sick person's name in deference to the concept that changing one's name changes one's *mazal*. Therefore, an additional advantage of praying for the sick person in his presence is that then one need not mention his name because the *Shechinah* is right there. The Chasam Sofer also mentions this concept in his *chiddushim* on the Gemara (*Nedarim* 40a). Obviously, a person telephoning a *choleh* is not able to completely fulfill the mitzvah of bikur cholim. The Yechaveh Daas concurs in this regard with the opinions of HaRav Moshe Feinstein (*Igros Moshe, Yoreh De'ah, Siman* 223) and the *Chelkas Yaakov* (2:128). However, if one is unable to visit the sick person, then certainly it is better to make a telephone call or write a letter to lift his spirits and fortify his hopes.

SELECTED RESPONSA FROM TZITZ ELIEZER

(R' Eliezer Waldenberg שליט"א)

≈§ Chelek 5, Ramat Rachel, Perek 2

- Is the mitzvah of bikur cholim included in the general command-ment of *gemilus chassadim* or is it a separate mitzvah?

The Tzitz Eliezer writes that one who reviews the mitzvos that have no prescribed measure, listed in the Mishnah (the first chapter of *Pe'ah*), will see that the mitzvah of bikur cholim is not included there. However, it is included in the Rabbis' statement that follows it, which we recite every morning during *Shacharis*. Bikur cholim is one of the mitzvos that benefit a person in this world as well as in the World to Come. This is based upon the Gemara (*Shabbos* 127a).

The *Aruch HaShulchan* writes that the mitzvah of bikur cholim is in-cluded in the general commandment of *gemilus chassadim*. However, the Tzitz Eliezer states that one could argue that it is a separate mitz-vah. Indeed, the *Baal Halachos Gedolos* and others do consider bikur cholim to be a separate mitzvah among the 613 mitzvos. Likewise, the *Leshon Chachamim* states that bikur cholim is a great mitzvah of *gemilus chassadim*, but that it is also a separate mitzvah in and of itself. Furthermore, the Tzitz Eliezer writes that the *She'iltos* (*Parashas Acharei Mos* 93) states explicitly that bikur cholim is a separate mitzvah in and of itself. The Rambam, however, disagrees with the *Baal Hala-chos Gedolos* and does not include it as a separate mitzvah, although he does include it as a separate Rabbinical commandment, distinct from the component of bikur cholim that is also a part of *gemilas chesed* per-formed with one's body. Indeed, the Rambam considers bikur cholim to be subsumed under the Torah's overarching precept of "*V'ahavta l'rei'acha kamocha*" (love your neighbor as you would yourself).

✑ Chelek 5, Ramat Rachel, Perek 3

- Further analysis of the status of the mitzvah of bikur cholim: Torah vs. Rabbinic precept

The Tzitz Eliezer resumes his analysis of the status of the mitzvah of bikur cholim: Is it a mitzvah *d'Oraisa* (of Biblical origin) or is it a mitzvah *d'Rabbanan* (of Rabbinic origin)? He cites the *Shelah,* who maintains that the mitzvah of bikur cholim is *d'Oraisa,* basing his opinion on the Gemara in *Nedarim* 40, where Rabbi Shimon discusses the origins of bikur cholim. The Tzitz Eliezer writes that the *Shelah* asserts, based on the explanation of the Rosh, that this is an explicit (Biblical) derivation rather than just an *asmachta* (an allusion; not a true Scriptural source). However, the Meiri asserts — based on the words of the *Sofrim* (Sages) — that the mitzvah of bikur cholim is *d'Rabbanan,* despite the allusions to it in the Torah.

✑ Chelek 5, Ramat Rachel, Perek 7

- How long should one wait to visit upon hearing that someone is sick?

This *teshuvah* discusses when it is appropriate to visit a sick person. Those closest to the sick person visit immediately; more casual acquaintances visit after a period of three days. The Tzitz Eliezer says that this is based upon a *Yerushalmi* (*Pe'ah* 3:7) and that the Ramban, the *Tur* and the *Shulchan Aruch* understood this *Yerushalmi* as referring to three complete days. In other words, if one is not close to the *choleh,* one should visit no sooner than the fourth day after hearing of the illness. However, the Tzitz Eliezer cites the

Rambam (*Hilchos Aveil* 14:5), who suggests that one can visit from the third day and onward. The Tzitz Eliezer believes that this is the Ramban's opinion as well. He concludes that this is also the opinion of the *sefer Shevet Yehudah,* written by the Mahari Eliash. The Tzitz Eliezer expresses surprise that great *sefarim* like the *Gesher HaChaim* state that one should not visit the sick until three days have passed. He concludes that this is incorrect.

ᵈᶳ Chelek 5, Ramat Rachel, Perek 12

- Appropriate time of day to visit a sick person
- Our custom is not to strictly adhere to the Gemara's admonition about not visiting the sick in the early or late hours of the day.

This *teshuvah* discusses the proper time of day to visit the sick. The *Shulchan Aruch* states that one should not visit the sick during the first three hours of the day, etc. [Ed. note: See translation of the *Shulchan Aruch* p. 138 §4 in this *sefer*.] The Tzitz Eliezer cites the *Aruch HaShulchan* [Ed. note: See translation of the *Aruch HaShulchan* p. 160 §8 in this *sefer*], who states that it is not *forbidden* to visit during those hours, but that it is merely sound advice and therefore we do not follow this practice today [Ed. note: because this no longer holds true today]. The Tzitz Eliezer is puzzled by the words of the *Aruch HaShulchan*. After all, the Gemara (*Nedarim* 40a) states in no uncertain terms that one should not visit the sick during those hours and explains why as well. [Ed. note: See our commentary on the *Shulchan Aruch* for these reasons.] How can the *Aruch HaShulchan* so blithely dismiss what appears to be a *halachah berurah* (clear-cut halachic decision)? The Tzitz Eliezer is left perplexed.

Furthermore, comments the Tzitz Eliezer, the main purpose of bikur cholim, according to the Gemara and the *Shulchan Aruch,* is to pray for the one who is ill. If one visits a sick person at the times when his condition appears most dire, one might despair of the patient's recovery. If so, Heaven forbid, the visitor will not *daven*

properly for the *choleh*, defeating the entire purpose of bikur cholim. Why then have we to some extent dismissed the Gemara's
halachah berurah? The Tzitz Eliezer suggests that this shift is based
upon the Rambam (*Hilchos Aveil* 14:5), who cites a different reason
than the despair the visitor will experience upon seeing the *choleh*
in such a sorry state. The Rambam writes that one should not visit
the sick in the early hours of the day since that is when their needs
are being attended to (the *Mishneh LaMelech* suggests that the
Rambam had a different version of our Gemara, one that did not
mention the despair factor).

Taking the Rambam's view into account, we can understand why
it is not considered an *issur* (forbidden), but merely good advice not
to visit in the morning; and certainly, if it would not disrupt the sick
person's care, one would be permitted to visit at that time. The Tzitz
Eliezer comments that it is astounding that the *Aruch HaShulchan*
did not cite this reason. (The Tzitz Eliezer writes that the *Birkei
Yosef* maintains that, indeed, this is the source one relies upon
when visiting during the hours that the Gemara deems inappropriate.) Alternatively, he quotes the *Shevet Yehudah,* who points out
that people go to work and may only have time in the morning to
visit the sick and, in fact, may be too tired to visit after work. In
addition, states the *Shevet Yehudah,* caregivers are aware that most
sick people will have visitors in the morning, and therefore this
would not interrupt their caregiving schedule.

However, one could argue with both of the *Shevet Yehudah's*
explanations. If people visit in the morning and tell themselves that,
despite the patient's more feeble appearance, they will nevertheless
beseech God to have mercy on him, one could argue that they may
nonetheless despair, partially thwarting the purpose of bikur cholim.
However, the Tzitz Eliezer suggests that it is sufficient merely to
request Hashem's mercy on the sick person's behalf; there is no
minimum requirement of fervor placed upon the visitors' prayers.
Regarding the *Shevet Yehudah's* second explanation, that caregivers
are aware that people will visit at those hours and that these visits will
not disrupt their work, this too could be questioned: Surely, the sick
person's needs cannot always be deferred to those of his visitors;
many needs will have to be met in the morning despite the caregiver's

willingness to address them at a later time. How could we ask care-givers to postpone their duties because we need to visit their patient?

The Tzitz Eliezer suggests that the Rambam, a physician of note, was acutely aware that the *choleh*'s needs could not be deferred. That is why the Rambam advised against visiting during those hours. Nevertheless, the Tzitz Eliezer concludes, based upon all of these explanations, one can be *melamed zechus* on (judge favorably) our custom not to follow zealously the Gemara's admonition about not visiting the sick in the early or late hours of the day. He concludes with a statement from the *Ahavas Chesed,* who writes that if one is unable to visit the *choleh* at any other time, it is better to visit him during these prescribed times rather than not do the mitzvah at all; hopefully, there will be some benefit, some improvement in the sick person's status, because of that visit.

Finally, the Tzitz Eliezer adds as an aside that the *Ahavas Chesed* points out that when we talk about the first and last three hours of the day, we are talking about *sha'os zemaniyos* (halachic hours based upon the length of daylight time divided into 12 equal "hours"). Otherwise, if one were not allowed to visit during a major portion of a short winter's day, there would barely be any time left to visit the sick.

⇜§ Chelek 5, Ramat Rachel, Perek 10

- Proper decorum with regard to sitting when visiting a sick person

The Tzitz Eliezer discusses the proper way to sit when visiting a sick person. Properly attired, visitors should sit in front of the sick person with trembling, awe and *yiras Shamayim,* looking into their own heart and trying to fathom what their future will be. This is so that the sick person should also experience these feelings and, con-sequently, repent with a full heart. However, the Tzitz Eliezer states that this certainly should not be done in a way that would terrify the *choleh* or cause him any pain; that would be prohibited.

ஃ Chelek 5, Ramat Rachel, Perek 10

- Appropriate dress when visiting the sick

In this *teshuvah* the Tzitz Eliezer discusses what exactly the *mechaber* of the *Shulchan Aruch* means when stating that one engaged in bikur cholim should cloak oneself (*mis'atef*) and sit in front of the *choleh* (*Siman* 335, Se'if 3). He cites the Shelah, who states that one should cloak oneself, just as one does in shul, out of respect for the *Shechinah*, Which is equally present in a shul and at a *choleh*'s bedside. There are those who suggest that this even includes wearing one's *tallis,* but the Tzitz Eliezer marshals commentators who suggest that it just means that one should dress in modest clothing, like a person approaching a king or entering a synagogue. Furthermore, the purpose of the cloaking discussed here is to show one's awe in the presence of the *Shechinah.* The *Birkei Yosef* states in the name of the *Shelah* that we do not cloak ourselves over our heads as our ancestors did [Ed. note: This mode of dress, which compels one to look straight ahead, minimizes distractions and prevents a person from glancing disrespectfully from side to side]. Thus, nowadays it would suffice to wear garments worn normally in shul, as a sign of respect when visiting the sick. And even though the word *mis'atef* implies *covering* the head, it is sufficient in our time — when it is not our custom to wear garments that cover our heads — to dress in the type of clothing one would wear in a shul.

In regard to the appropriate way to sit, visitors should do so in a way that exudes awe, respect, humility and fear of Hashem. When the *choleh* sees this, he will feel the need to do *teshuvah* with all his heart. However, one should not do this in a way that will frighten the *choleh* or cause him pain, because that is prohibited.

◄§ Chelek 5, Ramat Rachel, Perek 11

- Proper place to sit or stand when visiting a sick person

The Tzitz Eliezer states that visitors should never stand at the head of the bed (because that is where the *Shechinah* is positioned). When visiting an average person, one should not sit by his feet because it is possible that the Angel of Death is stationed in that area. In the second section of this *teshuvah*, the Tzitz Eliezer clarifies the *Shevet Yehudah's* commentary on *Yoreh De'ah* regarding three opinions about how to sit alongside the sick person's bed. The opinion of the *Shulchan Aruch* is that one should not sit higher than the head of the sick person. The opinion of the Rambam is that one should always sit lower than the head of the sick person, in terms of both the height and length of the bed. The most lenient opinion, that of *Tosafos,* is that one is permitted to sit adjacent to the sick person's head, albeit not higher than the head. The *Shevet Yehudah* rules according to the Rambam, the most stringent position's exponent. The Tzitz Eliezer concludes with the opinion of the Ritva: People have accepted the lenient position that one is even permitted to sit by the head of the *choleh,* even on a chair, as long as the visitor's chair is somewhat lower than the bed; and one may sit even at the same level as the bed, as long as one is not higher than it.

◄§ Chelek 17, Siman 100, Perek 10, Chelek 1

- Proper place to sit when visiting a sick person

The Tzitz Eliezer cites the *Zohar,* which comments in *Parashas Pinchas* that one should not sit by the foot of the bed of an average person who is ill, because the Angel of Death is there. However, if the sick person is righteous, one should specifically sit at the foot of the bed, because the *Shechinah* is present around the entire bed, except at the foot of the bed. The Tzitz Eliezer concludes with a statement from HaGaon Rav Fisher that when one is visiting a wicked person who is ill, anywhere one sits is dangerous. The Tzitz Eliezer writes that he is unsure whether the same ruling would apply to standing near a wicked *choleh*, and we are left without a definitive answer.

◄§ Chelek 5, Ramat Rachel, Perek 8

- A prestigious person is obligated to visit less respected sick people.
- There is no minimum or maximum duration to bikur cholim.
- Bikur cholim may be performed *bedi'eved* (suboptimally) via telephone
- One fulfills bikur cholim *bedi'eved* by inquiring about the sick person's welfare.

The Tzitz Eliezer also explores whether a greater person must visit a less prestigious person who is ill. In addition, he discusses the fact that there is no *shiur* (limit) to the mitzvah of bikur cholim, as well as the performance of this *chesed* via telephone.

He begins by citing Rashi (*Nedarim* 39b), who asserts that even a great person must visit a younger, less prestigious person. In other words, a person should not say, "I will only visit someone as great as myself." The Tzitz Eliezer then cites the *Ahavas Chesed,* who says that the simple understanding of Rashi is a reference to somebody chronologically younger than the age of bar mitzvah (who also must be visited). However, the *Ahavas Chesed* says that he himself understood this Rashi as a reference to someone who is beneath one's station, who nevertheless must be visited. The *Ahavas Chesed* suggests that this may be Rashi's intent as well. The Tzitz Eliezer then marshals many other *poskim* and proofs to support his position (using the expression, "Many prophets have prophesied the same thought as the *Ahavas Chesed*"), concluding that the simple understanding of the Gemara is that a greater person should visit a person of lower standing. He then cites a different version of the Gemara, quoted by the *Baal Halachos Gedolos,* which reads, "even a *gadol,* even a *katan,*" instead of "even a *gadol* has to visit a *katan.*" Obviously, the word *katan* in this context cannot mean that a child under the age of bar mitzvah is obligated to visit the sick, as there is never any mitzvah *obligation* for a child under bar/bas mitzvah. Therefore, since we must *visit* to be *mevaker cholim* even a *katan*, it must mean that one is obligated to visit a great person and even a person less prestigious than oneself.

However, this is problematic: Why did the Gemara have to state "even a *gadol*"? Obviously, if one has to visit a lesser person, one certainly would have to visit a greater person. The Tzitz Eliezer suggests that this is just an expression; you have to visit a great person or a less prestigious person. Alternatively, he suggests a novel interpretation: The phrase "even a *gadol*" is a reference to the duration of the visit. Whether one visits for a long period of time (*gadol*) or a short period of time (*katan*), one fulfills the obligation of bikur cholim throughout each and every second of the visit. Furthermore, even if one visits a sick person 100 times a day, each separate visit comprises a fulfillment of the mitzvah of bikur cholim. In other words, whether one visits for a short or long period of time, or even if one visits multiple times, one fulfills the mitzvah of bikur cholim every time and during every second that one is there.

The Tzitz Eliezer then states that he believes he found an allusion to his idea in the words of the Meiri, who also had a slightly different version of the Gemara. His version did not use the phrase "a great person with a lesser person," but rather "greater or lesser," which the Tzitz Eliezer suggests is referring to the duration of the visit. The Tzitz Eliezer furthermore states that in a situation where one is unable to visit the sick because of various obligations, including that of learning Torah (which is equivalent to all the other mitzvos combined), it appears that one may fulfill the mitzvah of bikur cholim by inquiring about the person's welfare from those who know him.

The Tzitz Eliezer concludes this *teshuvah* by discussing whether one can fulfill the obligation of bikur cholim via telephone. He posits that if the *choleh*'s needs are definitely being met (for example, if the *choleh* is in the hospital) [Ed. note: sadly, this may not always be the case in the hospital], and if one is informed of the patient's condition to a degree that will enable him to *daven* fervently on the patient's behalf, one could perform the mitzvah of bikur cholim via telephone. At least in this situation, one would not fall into the category of one who fails to fulfill this mitzvah.

◄§ Chelek 5, Ramat Rachel, Perek 8

- A greater person must go and visit a lesser person.
- There is no limit to the amount of bikur cholim that one can perform.
- If one is informed of the patient's condition to a degree that will enable him to *daven* fervently on the *choleh*'s behalf, one could perform the mitzvah of bikur cholim via telephone.

In this *teshuvah's* first section, the Tzitz Eliezer discusses the *Ahavas Chesed's* analysis of a Gemara (*Nedarim* 39b), which states that a *gadol* is required to visit a *katan* who is ill. Rashi comments that even a *gadol* has to visit a *katan*. The *Ahavas Chesed* explains that the simple understanding of Rashi is that a person has to visit even a child under the age of bar or bas mitzvah, but the *Ahavas Chesed* himself says that Rashi is referring not only to a *katan* in years, but to a sick person who is beneath the visitor's social and religious stature. Nevertheless, a greater person must go and visit a lesser person. We learn this from *HaKadosh Baruch Hu* Himself, who personally visited Avraham Avinu following his circumcision. The Tzitz Eliezer adds that the *Shitah Mekubetzes* and the *Shalmei Nedarim* agree with this opinion of the *Ahavas Chesed*. It differs from the exemption granted to an older person regarding the mitzvah of *hashavas aveidah*, where he is not obligated to return a lost item if it is beneath his dignity to do so. But in the case of bikur cholim, where even *HaKadosh Baruch Hu* Himself visited Avraham, a very respected person is obligated to visit a less respected person. This is the opinion of the *Birkei Yosef* as well.

In the next section of this *teshuvah*, the Tzitz Eliezer comments that there is no limit to the amount of bikur cholim that one can perform. Even 100 visits per day, as long as they do not tax the sick person, do not begin to fulfill the obligation of bikur cholim. This is a mitzvah that has no limit. Likewise, there is no limit to the duration of each visit; sometimes it is lengthy and sometimes it is brief.

✌ Chelek 5, Ramat Rachel, Perek 3

- One incapable of physically assisting or aiding the *choleh* is not exempt from visiting.
- One must pray on the sick person's behalf.

Since the key purpose of bikur cholim is to discern and meet the sick person's needs, the Tzitz Eliezer intimates that some might suggest that when one is absolutely certain that all of the sick person's needs are being met (for example, in a hospital setting), it is possible for one to be exempt from the obligation of bikur cholim. Indeed, from a superficial reading of the *Aruch HaShulchan,* who cites only this reason (helping the sick) as the purpose of bikur cholim, one might misunderstand and think that this is indeed the halachah. However, the Tzitz Eliezer strongly argues that such is not the case. The obligation to pray for the *choleh* is an equally important part of the mitzvah of bikur cholim, and this is optimally fulfilled at his bedside. Thus, the fact that one is not capable of physically assisting or aiding the *choleh* does not exempt one from visiting to pray on his behalf. [Ed. note: This understanding is consistent with the continuing mitzvah and importance of visiting a comatose patient receiving all of his physical needs in an intensive care hospital setting.]

❧ Chelek 5, Ramat Rachel, Perek 14

- Visiting the sick on Shabbos

The Tzitz Eliezer states here that one must further study the words of the *Shaarei Teshuvah,* found in *Orach Chaim* (287): A very softhearted person, who would suffer excessively with concern for the sick person, should not visit him on Shabbos because Shabbos was given for pleasure, not for suffering. [Ed. note: See the next *teshuvah*, where this is discussed in greater detail.]

❧ Chelek 13, Perek 36

- Visiting the sick on Shabbos
- The mitzvah of *oneg Shabbos* is overridden by the greater mitzvah of bikur cholim.
- When the *choleh* is in shul, it is preferble not to make a specific *mi shebeirach* for him.
- *Tefillah* for *cholim* recited on Shabbos
- Shabbos itself, and the *zechus* of *shemiras Shabbos*, protect the sick person.

Elaborating on the mitzvah of bikur cholim performed on Shabbos, the Tzitz Eliezer cites the Rambam, the *Tur* and the *Shulchan Aruch,* who all rule according to Beis Hillel (*Shabbos* 12b) that one is permitted to visit a sick person on Shabbos. They do not cite Rabbi Chanina's opinion that the Rabbis permit this only with difficulty, which implies that visiting the sick on Shabbos is not sanctioned wholeheartedly. However, the *Magen Avraham* does cite Rabbi Chanina's opinion that it was only with difficulty that the Rabbis permitted visiting the sick on Shabbos because of their concern that the visitor would be moved to tears. Therefore, the *Magen Avraham* opposes those who delay visiting the sick and do so *only* on Shabbos, as this could lead to problems according to the opinion of Rabbi Chanina. The *Shaarei Teshuvah* on the *Magen Avraham* expresses a similar idea, adding that a softhearted person should not visit the sick on Shabbos because it will diminish his *oneg Shabbos*, and Shabbos was given for pleasure, not pain. The Tzitz Eliezer marshals other sources here that suggest that he disagrees with the approach of the *Shaarei Teshuvah*. Indeed, the mitzvah of *oneg Shabbos* is overridden by the greater mitzvah of *bikur cholim*. In contrast to the *Shaarei Teshuvah*, the Tzitz Eliezer cites the *Levush* (*Siman* 287), who writes that the wish to minimize anguish on Shabbos is overridden by mitzvos of *gemilus chassadim*, such as *bikur cholim*. Indeed, says the Tzitz Eliezer, we do not rule according to Rabbi Chanina (that it is only with difficulty that the Rabbis permitted *bikur cholim* on Shabbos), but rather we say that even if it reduces *oneg Shabbos*, one still should visit the sick.

In the second half of *chelek beis* of this same *teshuvah*, the Tzitz Eliezer discusses whether it is permissible to make a *mi shebeirach* for a *choleh* in his or her presence. He states that, on the surface, it should be obvious that this is permissible, asking why there should be any difference between making a *mi shebeirach* in the presence or absence of a person. And indeed, he mentions having heard sick individuals request that the *gabbai* make a *mi shebeirach* in shul on their behalf. However, he then quotes the *mechaber*, Rabbi Yosef Karo, who states in the *She'eilos U'Teshuvos Avkas Rachel* (*Siman* 11) that his rebbi, the Mahari bei Rav, asserted that one should not make a *mi shebeirach* in the presence of a *choleh* since this might cause great suffering. The Tzitz Eliezer states that when the *choleh* is in shul, it is better not to make a specific *mi shebeirach* for him, but rather to make a general *mi shebeirach*, as is the custom after a person gets an *aliyah*, and to include that *choleh* among the people for whom one is davening. Alternatively, one may make a special *mi shebeirach* for him specifically after the *aliyah*. In addition, one should certainly have him in mind in the general *mi shebeirach* made for all the *cholim*. [Ed. note: In *Igros Moshe* (*Orach Chaim Chelek* 4 *Siman* 105), HaRav Moshe Feinstein states that it is permitted to make a *mi shebeirach* for a *choleh* who is present if the *choleh* requests it himself. This is permissible on Shabbos or Yom Tov as well, to prevent upsetting the *choleh* and possibly having a detrimental effect on his condition.]

At the conclusion of this *teshuvah*, the Tzitz Eliezer points out that *Chazal* specifically established a *tefillah* for *cholim* to be recited on Shabbos, despite the fact that there are many restrictions against utilizing medications and other therapies on Shabbos. He quotes one of the Chasam Sofer's *Shabbos Shuvah derashos* (*Parashas Ha'azinu*), which states that the *zechus* of Shabbos itself is so great that we should not specifically pray for an indiviual's *refuah sheleimah* on that day. The Chasam Sofer then asks: If this is so, how are we permitted to use any therapies on Shabbos? Yet, in fact, the halachah clearly allows one to treat a very sick person on Shabbos, and we do not say, "Let the *zechus* of Shabbos protect him." The answer, the Chasam Sofer affirms, is that when it comes to natural methods, we are obligated to do everything possible on Shabbos to save a person's life, and we do not say that the *zechus* of the mitzvah of *shemiras Shabbos* will protect that person. However, when it comes to asking *HaKadosh Baruch Hu* for assistance (for example, praying that He heal someone), even though this is a tried-and-true practice, one that we rely upon all the time, nevertheless we do not do this on Shabbos. Instead, we state that the Shabbos itself, and the *zechus* of *shemiras Shabbos,* will protect the sick person.

◈ Chelek 5, Ramat Rachel, Perek 6

- A visitor must not burden the sick person.
- Visiting people of average means, and certainly the poor and downtrodden, is especially important.
- Establishing a Chevrah Bikur Cholim (Bikur Cholim Society)

The Tzitz Eliezer writes that a visitor must not burden the *choleh*. This is based upon the Gemara (*Nedarim* 41b) that states that one may not visit a person with an intestinal illness, etc., because the sick person will be uncomfortable and embarrassed in the presence of the visitors. Unfortunately, adds the Tzitz Eliezer, many people have become lackadaisical regarding bikur cholim because of this concern. They are so concerned about the remote chance of having a negative impact upon the *choleh* that even when family members and caregivers state that the patient would welcome a visit, they stay away. This is a grave mistake based on faulty reasoning or erroneous self-serving rationale.

The Tzitz Eliezer cautions, however, that people should not visit a *choleh* if the visit will be burdensome to him. He cites the *Leshon Chachamim,* who writes that rich people — and prestigious people in general — might perceive as burdensome visitors whom they are not accustomed to receiving even when they are healthy. This would be true especially if the social status of the visitors was beneath theirs. From these visits, asserts the *Leshon Chachamim,* prestigious *cholim* would receive little comfort or benefit. However, he concludes that when it comes to visiting people of average means, and certainly the poor and downtrodden, the mitzvah of bikur cholim is doubled in importance. After all, these *cholim* may lack appropriate medical care as well as a support system of loved ones to beseech Hashem for mercy on their behalf. In addition, one is obligated to explore whether they have adequate financial resources, whether they need a loan or whether they need help to hire caregivers. Such acts of kindness often fall, quite literally, under the category of *pikuach nefesh*, the saving of a human life.

The Tzitz Eliezer concludes that, to counter any concerns that the one who is ill might have, each city should establish a Chevrah Bikur Cholim, whose holy purpose would be to visit the sick; to determine if their needs are being met; to arrange hospitalization for those who need it; and to assure *cholim* that caring people are davening on their behalf. This is similar to the Rambam's description of the mitzvah of escorting guests: In his day, the *beis din* would appoint messengers to escort guests from place to place. Since the obligation to be *mevaker cholim* is incumbent on every person, the Tzitz Eliezer's suggestion is especially appropriate for large cities, where it would be impossible for everyone to visit everyone.

≼ Chelek 5, Ramat Rachel, Perek 3

- Essential purpose of bikur cholim
- Identifying the sick person's needs and assisting him in whatever way is necessary
- Imploring Hashem for mercy on the sick person's behalf with our *tefillos*
- Visiting the sick alone or with other people
- Is speaking beneficial for the *choleh?*

This *teshuvah* explores the essential purpose of bikur cholim. The Tzitz Eliezer defines it as identifying the sick person's needs and assisting him in whatever way is necessary. Today, when those needs are frequently addressed fully by a hospital or healthcare facility, this essential component of bikur cholim may not be as applicable as it once was.

However, even if this essential component of bikur cholim is less germane, another critical component is always applicable: to beseech Heaven's mercy on the sick person's behalf with our *tefillos*. Indeed, the Ramban states that these two essential components of bikur cholim are intertwined and are, in fact, really one. He asserts that one who does not beg for Heaven's mercy on the sick person's behalf has not fulfilled the mitzvah of bikur cholim. Furthermore, awareness of his friends' and relatives' prayers will comfort the sick person; such comfort fulfills the third component of the mitzvah of bikur cholim. The Ramban's words are cited by the *Tur,* the *Beis Yosef,* the *Rema* and the *Aruch HaShulchan,* but the Tzitz Eliezer expresses surprise that the *Aruch HaShulchan* does not incorporate requesting Hashem's mercy on the *choleh*'s behalf as the most essential component of bikur cholim. Instead, the *Aruch HaShulchan* states that ascertaining the sick person's needs is the more important of the two.

The Tzitz Eliezer then cites the *Leshon Chachamim,* who states that the practice of large groups visiting *cholim* en masse on Shabbos, and saying that Shabbos will protect and save each *choleh*, is not ideal. Because of the size of the group, one does not truly ascertain the sick person's needs. Furthermore, one does not pray for the *choleh* at that time. [Ed. note: Personal supplications are usually not proffered on Shabbos, a day of sanctity on which personal concerns are set aside.] For these reasons, therefore, it is preferable that one should go alone on a weekday to visit a *choleh* in order to optimally inquire and pray regarding his immediate and far-reaching needs. The Tzitz Eliezer also quotes the *Sefer Chareidim's* assertion that conversation is good for the *choleh*. One should try to visit him particularly when no one else is there because, in his solitude, the *choleh* may become depressed, and this — *chas v'shalom* — could have a detrimental effect on his condition.

The Tzitz Eliezer expresses surprise that these very logical and rational guidelines are not cited in the *She'iltos* (*Vayikra* 93). Indeed, the opposite is written there, namely, that when one visits the sick, one should not go alone; one should always visit with other people. The Tzitz Eliezer suggests that this may be advised because two people might be able to assess and address the sick person's needs more effectively than one. Commenting on this *She'iltos,* the *Haamek She'eilah* states that the language of the *She'iltos* is to be found in no earlier halachic text; therefore, it must refer only to the unique case of visiting a sick person who is one's "*ben gilo*" [Ed. note: born at the same time; see *Nedarim* 39b for more information regarding a *ben gilo*]. However, the *Haamek She'eilah* does not believe this is the correct interpretation of the words of the *She'iltos*.

The Tzitz Eliezer concludes this *teshuvah* with a question on the *Divrei Charet,* a commentary on the *Sefer Chareidim,* who states that talking is beneficial for the *choleh*. This seems to contradict the Gemara (*Nedarim* 41a) that states that talking is taxing on the sick person's eyes (although it may be beneficial for a fever). Having investigated the *Sefer Chareidim's* source material, the Tzitz Eliezer states that they also agree that talking is good for a sick person who has a fever. This apparently was inadvertently omitted from the *Sefer Chareidim*.

❧ Chelek 5, Ramat Rachel, Perek 16

- Men visiting women and vice versa: required, permitted, prohibited?

This *teshuvah* deals with the statement in the *Aruch HaShulchan* (*Yoreh De'ah, Siman* 35, *Se'if* 11) that a man is permitted to visit a woman who is ill, and vice versa, as long as there is no inappropriate *yichud* (seclusion). The Tzitz Eliezer queries: What is the *Aruch HaShulchan's* source for this *din* (law) concerning men visiting women and women visiting men? After all, the *Shulchan Aruch* writes only that a man is not permitted to take care of a woman, but a woman is permitted to take care of a man, in cases of intestinal illness. From that assertion, the Tzitz Eliezer suggests that the *Aruch HaShulchan* infers that when the illness is not intestinal, one is permitted to visit a member of the opposite gender.

However, the Tzitz Eliezer disagrees with this proof. One could suggest that the *Shulchan Aruch* was dealing not with the mitzvah of bikur cholim but with the permissibility of a man taking care of an ill woman (or vice versa), but one cannot bring a proof that it is a mitzvah for a man to visit a woman (or vice versa). Therefore, the Tzitz Eliezer suggests that the *Aruch HaShulchan* was *mechadesh* (innovated) this *din* and that the normal concerns regarding inappropriate behavior between the two genders would not apply in a situation where one of them was sick. To ensure that the needs of the sick were being met, *Chazal* permitted opposite gender visitations and were not concerned about potential impropriety. However, this still does not fully explain why visiting ill members of the opposite gender always constitutes bikur cholim. Would it still be permissible if there were an adequate number of people of the same gender to meet the needs of the sick? Furthermore, the Tzitz Eliezer brings a proof from *Maseches Semachos* (*Perek* 12) that while it may be permissible for a man to attend to the needs of a woman (or vice versa) and one is not obligated to search for a person of the same gender for this task, nevertheless one cannot prove from this that visiting ill members of the opposite gender constitutes the mitzvah of bikur cholim.

The Tzitz Eliezer is further perplexed by the statement in the *sefer Zekan Aharon* (*Chelek 2, Siman 76*) that there is certainly a mitzvah, an obligation, for a man to visit a woman who is ill; not only to investigate her needs, but even to physically take care of her, if necessary. The Tzitz Eliezer reiterates that nowhere (not in the *Tur*, the *Levush* or other early halachic works) do we find a ruling that a man is obligated to visit a woman and vice versa, but only that it may be permissible for one to take care of a sick person of the opposite gender. Indeed, he writes, there is no source from which to derive an obligation of bikur cholim between members of the opposite gender.

The Tzitz Eliezer writes that he is very pained to argue with such prestigious authorities as the *Aruch HaShulchan* and the *Zekan Aharon* and therefore was overjoyed to find the *sefer Vayaan Avraham* (*Yoreh De'ah, Siman 5*), which notes that it is definitely *not* an obligation for a woman to visit a man. In fact, she should not visit a male patient unless he is one of those relatives with whom she is permitted to be alone. Similarly, a man should not visit a woman unless she is a relative with whom he is permitted to be alone. This ruling is not based on the laws of *yichud*, but rather on the fact that a man will not feel desire for female relatives with whom he is permitted to be alone and hence there is no concern of impropriety under those circumstances. This differs from a situation where one is visiting a non-relative of the opposite gender; then there is certainly a concern that improprieties might occur, and therefore such visits should not take place.

The *Vayaan Avraham* also discusses if, in general, a woman is obligated to visit another woman. One might posit that she be exempt, based on the principle (*Tehillim* 45:14): "*Kol kevudah bas melech penimah*," the very honor of a princess (i.e., the Jewish woman) is more internal [Ed. note: and thus, in general, she is not obligated to perform mitzvos that would require her to take on a public role]. However, the *Vayaan Avraham* concludes that a woman indeed is obligated to visit another sick woman because bikur cholim is a mitzvah that is not time-dependent. Furthermore, the Gemara states that if one visits a sick person, one receives Divine protection, and women have need of this as much as men. However, the *Vayaan Avraham* makes these exceptions: an expectant or nursing woman (who might find this mitzvah physically challenging or difficult), as well as one who has household responsibilities, or is needed by her husband, is not obligated to perform this mitzvah. The Tzitz Eliezer concludes that he concurs with the *Vayaan Avraham* and that there is definitely no obligation for a woman to visit a man, and that indeed it is preferable for her not to do so (and vice versa).

ᴥᴊ Chelek 5, Ramat Rachel, Perek 9

- Visiting a *choleh* for whom one feels hatred

The Tzitz Eliezer discusses the permissibility of visiting a *choleh* whom one hates. If indeed the *choleh* permits the one who hates him to visit, it is permissible — indeed, highly desirous — because hopefully this will lead to peace between them. In fact, some Rabbinic authorities write that nowadays our custom is to allow a person who hates a *choleh* to visit him. The Tzitz Eliezer cautions that, after all is said and done, one should not ignore the sage advice of the *Shach,* who writes that this all depends on the level of hatred between the parties concerned. He marshals support for the *Shach's* opinion by citing the *Shevet Yehudah,* who strongly concurs with the *Shach.* The Tzitz Eliezer concludes this *teshuvah* with a statement from the *Mateh Moshe:* As long as one's intentions are *l'shem Shamayim,* it is indeed advisable for a person who hates a *choleh* to visit him if this can potentially result in reconciliation.

ᴥᴊ Chelek 5, Ramat Rachel, Perek 27

- Reciting *Viddui* (confession prayer) as a component of bikur cholim
- The sick person should be reminded to put his/her affairs in order.
- Giving charity for a public need is especially appropriate for a sick person.

The Tzitz Eliezer states that even though *Chazal* prohibit us from causing any suffering to a *choleh*, they advise (*Shabbos* 32) that if he is near death, we must tell him to recite the *Viddui* (confession) prayer, even if it will pain him. This is because it is not proper for a person to die without reciting *Viddui*, an essential merit to accompany each soul as it enters the World to Come. The *Shelah*, in his commentary on *Maseches Pesachim*, includes *Viddui* as one of the components of bikur cholim. He offers the following *kal v'chomer* (an *a fortiori* inference): If the *chesed* of bikur cholim includes ensuring that the sick person's physical needs are met, then certainly one must ensure that his spiritual needs are met. One part of this responsibility is to advise him [Ed. note: when he is near death] to recite *Viddui* with a broken heart and true regret, beseeching Hashem to forgive him for his sins. Likewise, one must make sure that the *choleh*'s financial needs and affairs are in order, that he should neither be owed money nor owe money to someone else. An ill individual should not make that common, tragic mistake of waiting to discuss these matters until it is literally too late and he lacks the presence of mind or ability to address these spiritual and financial matters.

Continuing to cite the *Shelah*, the Tzitz Eliezer states that as soon as it appears that the *choleh* is in a potentially terminal situation, one should tell him that it is good to praise and beseech Hashem, the ultimate "Physician," and that *Viddui* is merely another form of *tefillah*, similar to that which we say every day in shul. Above all, the ill person should be told to request forgiveness from any person against whom he sinned, whether with words or actions (specifically financial in nature), because *HaKadosh Baruch Hu* is especially exacting over matters between man and his fellow man. Likewise, the *choleh* should be encouraged to forgive anyone who may have wronged him in any way, because if he does not forgive others, Heaven forbid, Hashem may not forgive him. Indeed, this is one of Judaism's cardinal rules: Those who forgive others are themselves forgiven. The ill person should then read *Viddui* exactly as it is found in most *siddurim*, word for word. If the *choleh* is a woman, she should specifically have in mind the three mitzvos that are uniquely hers: keeping the laws of family purity; separating the *challah* [Ed. note: separating a portion of dough as one of the 24 gifts to which a

Kohen in the time of the *Beis HaMikdash* was entitled; today in the absence of the Temple, the dough is burned instead]; and lighting the Shabbos candles. If she performed them improperly or inadequately, she should express her regret and state that if Hashem will heal her, she will make sure to perform them properly in the future. The Shelah concludes that the more often one recites *Viddui*, the better. The Tzitz Eliezer notes that other authorities assert that they frequently have seen a sick person improve physically after reciting *Viddui* and that the broken heart and spirit resulting from *Viddui* can benefit a person physically and spiritually.

The Tzitz Eliezer also cites the *Maavor Yabok*, who discusses the obligation upon a father to command his household — in front of witnesses — to divide up his property appropriately, especially when he knows that his children are prone to be confrontational and argumentative. The children are obligated to accept their father's directives and to interact with familial love and peace. The wise person will hear this and take it carefully to heart.

The Tzitz Eliezer then quotes the *sefer Ahavas Chesed,* by the Chofetz Chaim, which adds that one should remind a miserly or unkind person [Ed. note: one who was stingy and did not give charity generously or do acts of *chesed* during his lifetime] that it is never too late to mend one's ways. That person either should donate money now or at least resolve, without vowing, to correct his past behavior. This may actually spare his life for now and certainly will save him from the fires of Gehinnom. Likewise, the *Shevet Yehudah* states that it is appropriate for a person near death to contribute funds to poor people, to a *chesed* organization or to *hekdesh* (the *Beis HaMikdash*). The *Maavor Yabok* suggests that before reciting *Viddui*, one should — with his own hands — actually place money into a *tzeddakah* box or directly into the hands of a poor, worthy person. He recommends giving 26 (the *gematria* of the Tetragrammaton ‏י-ה-ו-ה‎), 91 (the *gematria* of ‏י-ה-ו-ה‎ plus the *Shem* of ‏א-ד-נ-י‎) or 112 (the *gematria* of those two Names plus the Name of Hashem known as ‏א-ה-י-ה‎) pennies. Of course, one may give more; and this may add days to the duration of his life.

The Tzitz Eliezer concludes by citing the sefer *Har Eival*: Giving charity for a public need is especially appropriate under these circumstances because it is very possible that one about to recite the *Viddui* is in possession of stolen money, money whose rightful owner he cannot identify [Ed. note: he does not know from whom he actually stole it]. The way to repent is to donate funds for the public good. Praiseworthy is the person who performs the mitzvah of bikur cholim and urges the ill person to do all of the above.

❧ Chelek 5, Ramat Rachel, Perek 34

- Appropriate conversation at the bedside of a patient who is near death

In the concluding statement of a complex *teshuvah* discussing various aspects of final care for a very sick person, the Tzitz Eliezer refers to the *Maavor Yabok,* who sharply exhorts those at the bedside of a *goseis* (an extremely sick person who is likely to die in the very near future). [Ed. note: The definition of a *goseis* is a very complicated halachic and medical enigma, beyond the scope of this work.] Those present must take every caution not to engage in *sichos beteilos* (unimportant, trivial conversations) and especially should avoid *divrei leitzanus v'kayotzei bahem* (silly, improper conversations and the like).

❧ Chelek 5, Ramat Rachel, Perek 4

- Praise of *chevros linah* volunteers providing nocturnal care for the sick
- Bikur cholim is a *chesed* done b'guf (body), b'nefesh (soul) and b'mamon) (money).

The Tzitz Eliezer strongly praises *chevros linah* [Ed. note: volunteers assigned to provide nocturnal care for the sick], groups that have been established in many cities to take care of the sick during the nighttime hours. This *chesed* is of greater necessity at night because the *choleh*'s relatives generally take care of him during the day but are exhausted and unable to do so at night. The Tzitz Eliezer cites the Chofetz Chaim, whose *sefer Ahavas Chesed* also extols the virtues of such groups. He calls them holy and states that they incorporate all of the wonderful character traits essential for *tzeddakah* and *chesed*. In fact, members of these groups perform acts of *tzeddakah* and *chesed* in two ways: for the *choleh* himself (by taking care of his needs when the exhausted family members are no longer able to do so) and for his relatives, at risk of becoming sick themselves due to the fatigue and stress that they endure while caring for the *choleh*. In effect, these righteous individuals are implementing *hatzalas nefashos rabbos* (the saving of many lives). Even if the *choleh* is wealthy and can afford to pay for round-the-clock care, it is possible that paid caregivers could not be found. Furthermore, even if he is able to find such caregivers, day and night coverage may exhaust them. Ultimately, the awareness of all the effort expended to help him recover will comfort and hearten the *choleh*. Praiseworthy is the city, the Chofetz Chaim concludes, that has such wonderful *baalei chesed* as the members of these *chevros linah*. [Ed. Note. Many communities have wonderful Bikur Cholim societies which to a large extent fulfill this function of *chevros linah*.]

The Tzitz Eliezer also cites Rabbi Raphael Mordechai Malki, a 16th-century Rav and physician of Yerushalayim, whose *Sefer Likkutim* mentions how fitting it is for each community in Israel to set aside a special bikur cholim charity fund. This fund would pay for physicians to care for and visit sick as well as poor people and, following the physicians' instructions, provide these people with food and their day-to-day necessities. The Tzitz Eliezer explains that this is why the Shelah writes in *Maseches Pesachim* that bikur cholim is a *chesed* done *b'guf, b'nefesh* and *b'mamon*: With one's *guf* (body), one should run and take care of all of the *choleh*'s needs, providing all the essential medications and therapies he will require; with one's *nefesh* (soul), one should pour out his heart and pray that Hashem will send the *choleh* a complete recovery; with one's *mamon* (money), one should help pay for the *choleh*'s treatments, which can prove extremely costly.

◄§ Chelek 5, Ramat Rachel, Perek 19

- Visiting mourners takes precedence over visiting the sick.
- If there is even the slightest concern that not visiting the *choleh* will cause him potential harm, visiting the sick takes precedence over comforting mourners.

This *teshuvah* begins with a statement from the *Aruch HaShulchan*: Visiting mourners takes precedence over visiting the sick because visiting *cholim* is only a *chesed* on behalf of the living, whereas comforting mourners is a *chesed* on behalf of both the living and the deceased. However, if one is doing something essential for the sick person, that activity would take precedence over visiting mourners. The Tzitz Eliezer expresses amazement that the *Aruch HaShulchan* does not cite the Rambam's declaration that this is true only when one cannot both visit the sick and comfort the mourners. However, the Rambam maintains that if one is able to do both mitzvos, then bikur cholim takes precedence so that the visitor can pray for mercy from Above (that the *choleh* may live) and/or to provide physical care for the *choleh*. He concludes that if one is unable to do both — even though this will prevent one from praying for the *choleh* or from taking care of his physical needs — comforting mourners takes precedence. This is the opposite of what the *Aruch HaShulchan* seems to imply.

However, the Tzitz Eliezer quotes the *Radvaz*, who states that were it not for the Rambam, he would have said the opposite: that visiting the sick takes precedence over visiting mourners, because not visiting the sick is equivalent to murder, as is stated in the Gemara, and that is exactly why the *Beis Yosef* does not cite this Rambam *l'halachah* in his *sefer*. However, the *Rema*, the *Bach*, the *Shach*, the *Levush* and the *Aruch HaShulchan* all cite this Rambam *l'halachah*: that *nichum aveilim* (comforting mourners) takes precedence over bikur cholim.

The Tzitz Eliezer, however, does find support for the *Aruch HaShulchan* from the *Leshon Chachamim* (*Chelek* 2, *Siman* 25), citing the *Tiferes L'Moshe,* who is also surprised by the Rambam's ruling, because if one does not take care of the *choleh,* he might not survive. This revises the scenario to one of *pikuach nefesh* (saving a life), a mitzvah of paramount importance that supersedes the obligation to visit and comfort mourners. Therefore, the *Leshon Chachamim* suggests that the Rambam is referring only to a case where all the *choleh*'s physical needs are met and the visitor's only purpose is to pray for and comfort him. Ostensibly, this is not how the Bach understood the Rambam.

The Tzitz Eliezer concludes, however, that clearly — according to the *Bach,* the *Shach* and the *Chochmas Adam* — the halachah that visiting and comforting mourners takes precedence over visiting and comforting the sick refers only to "routine" bikur cholim, performed to fulfill the obligation to visit the sick, which may lead incidentally to some slight improvement in the *choleh*'s care. If there is even the slightest concern that not visiting the *choleh* will cause him potential harm or even his demise, everybody certainly agrees that visiting the sick takes precedence over visiting and comforting mourners. This is essentially the *psak,* ruling, of the *Aruch HaShulchan.*

Talmudic Sources

Shabbos 12a

וְאֵין מְבַקְּרִין חוֹלִין בְּשַׁבָּת – **And one may not visit the sick on the Sabbath.**[1] דִּבְרֵי בֵּית שַׁמַּאי – These are **the words of Beis Shammai;** וּבֵית הִלֵּל מַתִּירִין – **but Beis Hillel permit** these activities on the Sabbath.[2]

The Gemara cites a Baraisa about visiting the sick on the Sabbath:

תָּנוּ רַבָּנָן – **The Sages taught in a Baraisa:** הַנִּכְנָס לְבַקֵּר אֶת הַחוֹלֶה אוֹמֵר – **One who enters to visit a sick person** on the Sabbath **should say:** שַׁבָּת הִיא מִלִּזְעוֹק – **"The Shabbath** prevents us **from crying out** for your recovery, **but recovery will come soon."**[3] וְרַבִּי מֵאִיר אוֹמֵר – **And R' Meir says:** יְכוֹלָה הִיא שֶׁתְּרַחֵם – One should say: **"[The Sabbath]** itself **can have mercy** and bring your recovery."[4]

NOTES

1. These activities are prohibited because they cause anguish (*Rashi;* see *Rif* and *Ran*).

2. According to Beis Hillel, the verse in *Isaiah* specifies *"your* business" to teach that only business commitments for personal needs are forbidden, while business commitments for the purpose of a mitzvah are permitted. Therefore, arranging for a child to be married or taught a craft, which is a mitzvah, is permitted on the Sabbath (*Rashi,* from Gemara below, 150a). [Ensuring that one's son learns a craft is a mitzvah, because without a craft for his livelihood, he may resort to stealing (*Rashi* ibid., from *Kiddushin* 30b).]

Beis Hillel also reject the prohibitions against visiting the sick and consoling mourners, because these are acts of kindness, and the visit will help relieve the pain of the sick and the mourning (*Aruch HaShulchan, Orach Chaim* 287:1).

3. We are not allowed to pray to God on his behalf, because such prayer would arouse weeping and sorrow. Instead, we offer him words of hope to lift his spirits (*Ran*).

A sick person might mistakenly believe that the Sabbath delays his recovery, because were it not for the Sabbath people would pray for him. We therefore reassure him by saying that although praying is prohibited on the Sabbath, "recovery will come soon." His recovery is as likely to be granted on the Sabbath [without prayer] as it is during the week [with prayer] (*Maharsha*).

When visiting mourners, one should say שַׁבָּת הִיא מִלְּנַחֵם וְנֶחָמָה קְרוּבָה לָבֹא, *The Sabbath* [prevents us] *from consoling* [you], *but consolation will come soon* (*Mishnah Berurah* 287:3; see there).

4. The sick person is told that if he honors the Sabbath by ignoring his pain, perhaps in that very merit he will be healed soon (see *Rashi* and *Rif*).

Here, the point is explicitly made that the Sabbath does not delay recovery. On the contrary, it can hasten recovery even without the aid of prayer (*Maharsha;* see previous note).

רַבִּי יְהוּדָה אוֹמֵר – **R' Yehudah says:** הַמָּקוֹם יְרַחֵם עָלֶיךָ וְעַל חוֹלֵי יִשְׂרָאֵל – One should say: **"May the Omnipresent have mercy on you and on the sick of Israel."**

רַבִּי יוֹסֵי אוֹמֵר – **R' Yose says:** הַמָּקוֹם יְרַחֵם עָלֶיךָ בְּתוֹךְ חוֹלֵי יִשְׂרָאֵל – One should say: **"May the Omnipresent have mercy on you among the sick of Israel."**[1]

שֶׁבְנָא אִישׁ יְרוּשָׁלַיִם בִּכְנִיסָתוֹ אוֹמֵר – **When Shevna, a prominent person in Jerusalem, would enter** to visit a sick person on the Sabbath, **he would say:** שַׁבָּת הִיא **"Peace";** וּבִיצִיאָתוֹ אוֹמֵר – **and when leaving, he would say:** שָׁלוֹם מִלִּזְעוֹק וּרְפוּאָה קְרוֹבָה לָבֹא – **"The Sabbath** prevents us **from crying out** for your recovery, **but recovery will come soon.** וְרַחֲמָיו מְרוּבִּין – **[God's] mercies are many,** וְשִׁבְתּוּ בְשָׁלוֹם – **and rest** on the Sabbath **in peace."**[2]

The Gemara specifies which of these Tannaic opinions is the source for the following Amoraic statement:

כְּמַאן אַזְלָא הָא דְּאָמַר רַבִּי חֲנִינָא – **With whom does this teaching** stated by **R' Chanina accord?** מִי שֶׁיֵּשׁ לוֹ חוֹלֶה בְּתוֹךְ בֵּיתוֹ – **One who has a sick person in his household** צָרִיךְ שֶׁיְּעָרְבֶנּוּ בְּתוֹךְ חוֹלֵי יִשְׂרָאֵל – **must include him together with the sick of Israel** when praying on his behalf. כְּמַאן – **With whom** does this teaching **accord?** כְּרַבִּי יוֹסֵי – It **accords with R' Yose.**[3]

The Gemara cites another teaching by R' Chanina on this topic:

וְאָמַר רַבִּי חֲנִינָא – **And R' Chanina said:** בְּקֹשִׁי הִתִּירוּ לְנַחֵם אֲבֵלִים וּלְבַקֵּר חוֹלִים בְּשַׁבָּת – It was **with difficulty** that **[the Rabbis] permitted** one to **console mourners and to visit the sick on the Sabbath.**[4]

The Gemara records how a certain sage would address a sick person during the week:

אָמַר רַבָּה בַּר בַּר חָנָה – **Rabbah bar bar Chanah said:** כִּי הֲוָה אַזְלִינַן בַּתְרֵיהּ דְּרַבִּי

NOTES

1. R' Yose recommends a formula that groups this sick person together with others, because a prayer offered on behalf of many people is more likely to be accepted (*Rashi*). [In R' Yose's opinion, the formula proposed by R' Yehudah is essentially a dual prayer — one for this sick person and one for others.]

R' Yehudah and R' Yose presumably agree with the previously quoted Tannaim, who hold that one may not pray for a sick person on the Sabbath. Still, these words are permitted, for since they are directed to the sick person and not to God, they do not constitute real prayer (*Maharsha*).

2. God's mercy is so great that He will heal you even without our prayers. All that you have to do is observe the Sabbath in peace.

Shevna states that one should begin and end his visit with the word שָׁלוֹם, *shalom* (peace). Although praying to God on behalf of a sick person is prohibited on the Sabbath, one is allowed to greet him with the word *shalom,* which is a Name of God [see above, 10b] (*Maharsha*).

3. The word יְעָרְבֶנּוּ, *he should include him,* indicates that he should pray for them together, and not as two distinct entities. This conforms to the view of R' Yose (see note 1).

4. Because the visitor feels distress (*Rashi*).

אֶלְעָזָר לְשַׁוּוּלֵי בִּתְפִיחָה – **When we would go with R' Elazar to visit a sick person,** we noticed that זִימְנִין אָמַר הַמָּקוֹם יִפְקָדְךָ לְשָׁלוֹם – **sometimes he said, "May God remember you for peace"** in Hebrew, וְזִימְנִין אָמַר (לֵיהּ) רַחֲמָנָא יִדְכְּרִינָךְ לִשְׁלַם – **and sometimes he said, "May the Merciful One remember you for peace"** in Aramaic.[5]

The Gemara asks:

הֵיכִי עָבִיד הָכִי – **How could he have done this?** That is, how could R' Elazar have prayed in Aramaic? וְהָאָמַר רַב יְהוּדָה – **But Rav Yehudah has said:** לְעוֹלָם אַל יִשְׁאַל אָדָם צְרָכָיו בִּלְשׁוֹן אֲרַמִּי – **A person should never request his needs** from God **in Aramaic.** וְאָמַר רַבִּי יוֹחָנָן – **And R' Yochanan said:** כָּל הַשּׁוֹאֵל צְרָכָיו בִּלְשׁוֹן אֲרַמִּי – **If anyone requests his needs in Aramaic,** אֵין מַלְאֲכֵי הַשָּׁרֵת נִזְקָקִין לוֹ – **the ministering angels do not pay attention to him,** שֶׁאֵין מַלְאֲכֵי הַשָּׁרֵת מַכִּירִין בִּלְשׁוֹן אֲרַמִּי – **because the ministering angels do not know Aramaic.**[6]

NOTES

5. If the patient understood Hebrew, R' Elazar would speak to him in that language. Otherwise, he would use Aramaic, which was the vernacular (*Hagahos R' Elazar Moshe Horowitz;* see also *Chasam Sofer*).

6. An individual [as opposed to a community] requires the assistance of the ministering angels for his prayers to reach God (*Rashi* to *Sotah* 33a ד"ה יחיד; see also *Rabbeinu Yonah* to *Berachos* folio 7a ד"ה אבל ביחיד; see, however, the opinions cited below).

R' Yochanan states that the ministering angels do not understand Aramaic. Some commentators explain this to mean that they do not understand *even* Aramaic, which is the language closest to Hebrew, and certainly not any other language. The only language they know is *Hebrew* (*Levush, Orach Chaim* 101:7, as explained by *Eliyahu Rabbah* ibid.; cf. *Chasam Sofer* here). Another view is that in fact the angels understand *all* the languages (see *Tosafos, Eliyahu Rabbah* ibid. 8 and *Sfas Emes*). However, they do not pay attention to prayers delivered in Aramaic, because Aramaic is unseemly to them, being a corrupt form of Hebrew (*Rosh* and *Rabbeinu Yonah* to *Berachos* ibid.; see *Raavad* in *Temim De'im* 185; see also *Shulchan Aruch Orach Chaim* 101:4 with *Chochmas Shlomo*). According to this approach, the term אֵין ... מַכִּירִין means *they do not like* (see *Eitz Yosef*).

HaKoseiv (on *Ein Yaakov*) raises the following problem: This Gemara is difficult to understand in light of the fact that we may not include mention of any intercessor in our prayers.

In the fifth of his Thirteen Principles of Faith, *Rambam* writes: "It is the Blessed One Whom it is proper to worship, to exalt, to propagate His greatness, and to fulfill His commandments. But one must not do so for anything of lower existence [than God Himself], such as the angels, the stars, the spheres, the elements and whatever is composed of them ... It is likewise improper to pray that they act as intercessors to present [our prayers] to Him. Only to Him shall one's thoughts be directed; and all besides Him should be ignored ..." (*Commentary to the Mishnah, Sanhedrin* Ch.10).

Ramban writes similarly: "The third form of idolatry is considering the angels capable of serving as intermediaries between God and His worshipers ... Realize that even to pray to them for this purpose is forbidden to us ..." (*Toras Hashem Temimah*). [Regarding the propriety of *piyutim* addressed to angelic advocates, see *Mavo* to *Siddur Otzar HaTefillos,* section 3, למי מתפללין.]

How do these Rishonim explain our Gemara's teaching that a prayer in Aramaic is ineffectual because the angels do not pay attention to it?

HaKoseiv answers as follows: The angels referred to here are those who carry out

The Gemara explains how R' Elazar could pray in Aramaic:

שָׁאנֵי חוֹלֶה – A sick person is different, דִּשְׁכִינָה עִמּוֹ – because the Divine Presence is with him.[7] דְּאָמַר רַב עָנָן אָמַר רַב – As Rav Anan said in the name of Rav: מְנַיִן שֶׁשְּׁכִינָה סוֹעֵד אֶת הַחוֹלֶה – From where is it derived that the Divine Presence supports a sick person? שֶׁנֶּאֱמַר ,,ה' יִסְעָדֶנּוּ עַל-עֶרֶשׂ דְּוָי" – For it is stated:[8] *Hashem will support him on the sickbed.*

NOTES

God's will *in response* to prayer. These angels are not likely to be called upon to "pay attention to" (i.e. fulfill the request of) one who prays in Aramaic. The reason is that since Aramaic is the commonly spoken language, such prayer tends to be recited mechanically, without feeling and devotion. A prayer in Hebrew, however, is accepted even if it is not delivered with the full measure of concentration, because, as the "Holy Tongue," Hebrew has a unique power to elevate prayers to Heaven (see *Beur Halachah* to 101:4 ד"ה יכול).

Meiri maintains that the Gemara is not literal. Rather, in a poetic style, it is teaching that prayers in Aramaic [or any language other than Hebrew] are less likely to be accepted. Since people are not used to [praying in] Aramaic, one who prays in this language tends to lack the degree of devotion required for his prayer to be heeded.

7. Since the Divine Presence is present at a sickbed, one who prays [there] does not require the ministering angels to relay his prayers to God (*Rashi*). [For the same reason, one who prays together with the community may use any language, because God Himself attends the prayers of the community (*Sotah* 33a; see *Shulchan Aruch Orach Chaim* 101:4 for the details of this law).]

The previous teaching – namely, that a prayer in Aramaic (or any language besides Hebrew) is ineffectual – applies only where the prayer is transmitted through angelic intermediaries, and not where one's prayer reaches God directly. This can be understood using the analogy of a human king. When submitting a request to the king through his servants, one must follow the official rules, because otherwise the servants are not authorized to forward the request to the king. The king himself, however, can waive the rules. Therefore, when speaking to the king personally, one may express oneself in whatever manner is most effective, even if that does not conform to the official protocol. Likewise, when beseeching the King of kings, one may use the language in which one's entreaties will be most heartfelt and pure (*Chasam Sofer*).

According to *Meiri* (see previous note), the Gemara's point is that when one beseeches God to heal a sick person, he surely prays with great fervor. It is as though his heart is automatically directed to God. (This is the meaning of "the Divine Presence is with him.") In such a circumstance, it makes no difference which language he uses. Likewise, one who prays with the community is inspired to a higher level of devotion and consequently he too may use any language.

8. *Psalms* 41:4. God supports the sick person who lacks the strength to do so himself (see *Rashi*).

Rashi mentions an alternative text: מְנַיִן שֶׁשְּׁכִינָה סוֹעֵר אֶת הַחוֹלֶה, *From where is it derived that the Divine Presence visits a sick person?* שֶׁנֶּאֱמַר ,,ה' יִסְעָדֶנּוּ עַל-עֶרֶשׂ דְּוָי", *As it is stated:* "*Hashem will support him (yisadenu) on the sickbed.*" אַל תִּקְרֵי יִסְעָדֶנּוּ אֶלָּא יִסְעָרֶנּוּ, *Do not read "yisadenu"* (support him), *but rather "yisarenu"* (visit him). This version is also cited by *Aruch* (ע' סר [ב]). [The word סוֹעֵר, translated here as "visit" (בקור), derives from the word סָר, which means to *inspect* or *examine*. Indeed, it is clear from the ruling of *Shulchan Aruch* (*Yoreh Deah* 335:8) that one of the primary purposes of visiting a sick person (בקור חולים) is to determine his needs so that they can be provided for.]

הַנִּכְנָס לְבַקֵּר אֶת הַחוֹלֶה – **And this was also taught in a Baraisa:** תַּנְיָא נַמִי הָכִי **One who enters to visit a sick person** לֹא יֵשֵׁב לֹא עַל גַּבֵּי מִטָּה וְלֹא עַל גַּבֵּי כִּסֵּא **should not sit on a bed or on a chair.**[9] אֶלָּא מִתְעַטֵּף וְיוֹשֵׁב לְפָנָיו – **Rather, he should wrap himself**[10] **and sit before him,**[11] מִפְּנֵי שֶׁשְּׁכִינָה לְמַעְלָה מֵרַאֲשׁוֹתָיו שֶׁל חוֹלֶה – **because the Divine Presence is above the head of a sick person,** שֶׁנֶּאֱמַר ,,ה׳ יִסְעָדֶנּוּ עַל-עֶרֶשׂ דְּוָי" – **as it is stated:** *Hashem will support him on the sickbed.*

A similar teaching:

וְאָמַר רָבָא אָמַר רָבִין – **Rava said in the name of Ravin:** מִנַּיִן שֶׁהַקָּדוֹשׁ בָּרוּךְ הוּא זָן אֶת הַחוֹלֶה – **From where is it derived that the Holy One, Blessed is He, sustains a sick person?** שֶׁנֶּאֱמַר ,,ה׳ יִסְעָדֶנּוּ עַל-עֶרֶשׂ דְּוָי" – **For it is stated:** *Hashem will support him on the sickbed.*[12]

NOTES

9. This restriction applies only where the sick person is lying on the ground or on a low bed. In such a case, if the visitor were to sit on a chair, he would be "higher" than the Divine Presence, which is at the patient's head (*Tosafos; Ran* to *Nedarim* 40a; *Rama* to *Yoreh Deah* 335:3; see *Beis Hillel* ibid. and *Aruch HaShulchan* ibid. 7).

Meiri explains that when the patient sees his visitor manifesting fear of Heaven, he will be motivated to turn to God in sincere repentance.

10. This too is a sign of reverence for the Divine Presence. By covering his head he limits his view, and thus he sits in the manner of an awestruck person, who does not glance about (*Rashi*).

11. [On the ground or on a chair lower than the sick person's head (see note 9).]

12. [The verb סעד can also denote support in the sense of providing sustenance and nourishment. סְעוּדָה, *meal,* is derived from this root.]

Nedarim 39b

The Gemara digresses to discuss the topic of visiting the sick:

אָמַר רֵישׁ לָקִישׁ – **Reish Lakish said:** רֶמֶז לְבִיקוּר חוֹלִין מִן הַתּוֹרָה מְנַּיִן – **Where in the Torah may we find an allusion to the** mitzvah of **visiting the sick?**[1] In the following verse,[2] שֶׁנֶּאֱמַר – **as it says:**[3] ,,אִם־כְּמוֹת כָּל־הָאָדָם יְמֻתוּן אֵלֶּה – *Moses*

NOTES

1. The term for visiting the sick in Hebrew is בִּיקוּר חוֹלִים, *bikur cholim*. The root בקר means to check and to tend to. Thus, we find (*Ezekiel* 34:12): כְּבַקָּרַת רֹעֶה עֶדְרוֹ ... כֵּן אֲבַקֵּר אֶת־צֹאנִי, *As a shepherd tends to his flock . . . so I will tend to My sheep* (see also *Chullin* 32a with *Rashi* ד"ה כדי ביקור חכם). The essence of *bikur cholim* is to find out what needs the sick person may have that are not being cared for and to attend to them (see *Ramban, Toras HaAdam, Shaar HaMichush;* see also below, 40a, with *Rosh* ד"ה שכבר and *Maharsha* ד"ה שנאמר; *Geon Yaakov* ד"ה אר"י אמר שמואל).

In the same vein, *Ramban* (loc. cit.) rules that whoever visits a sick person but does not pray on his behalf has not fulfilled the mitzvah (see *Rama, Yoreh Deah* 335:4). [However, even if the sick person has no concrete needs that the visitor could attend to,] the visitor performs the mitzvah of *bikur cholim* by merely making an appearance and allowing the sick person to enjoy his company. In the same passage where Ramban highlights the importance of prayer, he also lists as one of the aims of *bikur cholim* to give the sick person the opportunity to find satisfaction with his friends (see also *Meiri; Shitah Mekubetzes* cited below, note 48; see *Maharsha* to *Bava Metzia* 30b ד"ה והודעת, who says one can fulfill the mitzvah of visiting the sick by simply going there).

In an unpublished medical manuscript (cited in *Einayim LaMishpat*), *Rambam* writes: [Those in attendance are] to relate to the sick person encouraging stories that will expand his soul and expand his heart, and [they are] to come up with new thoughts that will distract his mind [from his suffering] and allow him to laugh about them, he and his entire group. And they should choose to serve him and to stand before him someone with whom he will be happy. All of this is obligatory for every illness.

In his commentary to the Torah (*Genesis* 18:1), *Rosh* states that one should visit a sick person even if he will not be able to speak to him, e.g. he found him asleep. In this case, the sick person will be pleased when he awakens and they tell him that So-and-so came to see him.

2. The Gemara elsewhere (*Bava Kamma* 100a, *Bava Metzia* 30b) finds a Scriptural allusion to visiting the sick that is different from the one our Gemara is about to expound. Our Gemara is aware of that allusion, but the verse upon which that allusion is based does not refer explicitly to sick people or visiting them. Our Gemara therefore searches for a more explicit allusion (*Rosh*).

Regardless of a specific reference to the mitzvah of visiting the sick, one fulfills two general mitzvos when one does so. First of all, one has performed a kindness for a fellow human being (*Bava Metzia* 30b) and has therefore fulfilled the mitzvah (*Leviticus* 19:18): וְאָהַבְתָּ לְרֵעֲךָ כָּמוֹךָ, *You shall love your fellow as yourself.* This mitzvah encompasses all favors performed for others that we would wish to be performed for us (*Rambam, Sefer HaMitzvos, shoresh* 2 ד"ה וכבר הגיע בהם and *Hil. Aveil* 14:1; *Ramban, Hasagos* to *Sefer HaMitzvos, shoresh* 1 ד"ה והתשובה הרביעית). Second, one fulfills the mitzvah of emulating God in His noble ways, as it says (*Deuteronomy* 13:5): אַחֲרֵי ה' אֱלֹהֵיכֶם תֵּלֵכוּ, *You shall follow Hashem, your God.* [There are seven other verses that convey the same idea — see *Introduction to Ahavas Chesed*.] Thus, the Gemara in *said ... **If these** [people] **die the death of all men*** "וגו' וּפְקֻדַּת כָּל־[הָ]אָדָם" – *and* **the visitation of all men etc.,** *is visited upon them.*[4]

The Gemara inquires:

מַאי מַשְׁמַע – **How does [this verse] imply** that there is a mitzvah to visit the sick? How is Reish Lakish expounding this verse?

The Gemara explains:

אָמַר רָבָא: – **Rava said:** "אִם־כְּמוֹת כָּל־הָאָדָם יְמֻתוּן אֵלֶּה" – ***If these** [people] **die the death of all men*** means שֶׁהֵן חוֹלִים וּמוּטָלִים בַּעֲרִיסָתָן – **that [Korach and his followers] would take ill and become bedridden** [when they grow old], as is typical for someone approaching death, *and the visitation of all men is visited upon them* means וּבְנֵי אָדָם מְבַקְּרִים אוֹתָן – **that people visit them** to inquire after their welfare and to see if they may be of assistance.[5] We therefore find an

---

NOTES

Sotah 14a teaches that just as we find that God visited Abraham when he was ill, so too should we visit people when they are ill, etc. (*Ramban* loc. cit.; see *Rambam, Sefer HaMitzvos, Asei* 8 and *Hil. Dei'os* 1:5-6; *Sefer HaChinuch* 611).

[Whenever a person performs an act of kindness, he also fulfills the mitzvah of emulating God; it appears, however, that these two mitzvos differ in their focus. The point of kindness is to benefit others; the point of going in God's ways is to make oneself into a better, more Godlike person. It should also be noted that, at least according to *Rambam,* although one fulfills the general Biblical mitzvah of kindness when one visits the sick or clothes the naked or comforts mourners, the obligation to do these *specific* acts is Rabbinical (*Sefer HaMitzvos, shoresh* 2; *Kiryas Sefer, Hil. Aveil* Ch. 14). Accordingly, the Scriptural allusion to the mitzvah of visiting the sick that the Gemara now proceeds to expound is not a full-fledged exposition (see *Maharatz Chayes,* citing *Rambam*).]

3. *Numbers* 16:29.

4. The background to Moses' statement is as follows: Moses had appointed certain people to positions of prominence (e.g. his brother Aaron as Kohen Gadol) and Korach and his followers disputed these appointments (see *Midrash Tanchuma, Korach* 1 and *Rashi* to *Numbers* 16:1-3). They claimed that Moses had not acted at God's direction but had rather fabricated his own instructions. Korach's faction succeeded in turning a significant segment of the Jewish people against Moses. After attempting again and again to settle the controversy peacefully, Moses was forced to demonstrate his Divine authorization and punish the wrongdoers. The Torah relates (*Numbers* 16:28-33): Moses said, *"Through this shall you know that Hashem sent me to perform all these acts, that it was not [a fabrication] of my heart: If these [people] die the death of all men, and the visitation of all men is visited upon them, then it is not Hashem Who has sent me. But if Hashem will create a phenomenon, and the earth opens its mouth and swallows them and all that is theirs, and they will descend alive to the pit — then you shall know that these men have provoked Hashem!" When he finished speaking all these words, the ground that was under them split open. The earth opened its mouth and swallowed them and their households, and all the people who were with Korach, and the entire estate. They and all that was theirs descended alive to the pit. The earth covered them over and they were lost from among the congregation.*

5. According to the plain meaning of the verse, the words וּפְקֻדַּת כָּל-הָאָדָם יִפָּקֵד עֲלֵיהֶם mean *the destiny of all men is visited upon them,* i.e. they die a natural death. But the Gemara interprets the words וּפְקֻדַּת ... יִפָּקֵד to mean that [if Moses fabricated his instructions] the acquaintances of Korach's followers will be able to visit them as they lie bedridden in their

allusion to the mitzvah of visiting the sick in Moses' warning regarding Korach and his followers.

The Gemara continues with an explanation of the end of the verse:

מָה הַבְּרִיּוֹת אוֹמְרִים – **What would people say,** Moses asked rhetorically, if Korach and his followers would not die a miraculously sudden death as I am predicting? They would say that לֹא ה' שְׁלָחַנִי לָזֶה – **God never sent me to** make **these** appointments which Korach's faction opposes.[6]

Rava expounds the ensuing verses:

NOTES

final illness (see *Ran, Tosafos, Mefaresh*). According to this interpretation, Moses was saying that the death of Korach et al. would be sudden and therefore not preceded by sickness and friendly visits. Since Moses referred to the practice of visiting the sick, it must be that this is what people do (*Shitah Mekubetzes*). [The root פקד has several meanings, one of which is to attend to or oversee something (*Ibn Janach* in the introduction to *Sefer HaShorashim* and in ערך פקד), as in the verse (*I Samuel* 17:18): וְאֶת-אַחֶיךָ תִּפְקֹד לְשָׁלוֹם, *and you shall inquire after the welfare of your brothers*. Thus, our verse means: וּפְקֻדַּת כָּל-הָאָדָם, just as all people who take ill before dying are attended to by their friends, יִפָּקֵד עֲלֵיהֶם, so too will they be attended to when they take ill.]

Ben Yehoyada explains how the concept of visiting the sick was relevant to Korach's downfall: An important purpose of visiting the sick is to ameliorate the sick person's suffering. The Gemara says below that the visitor of a sick person takes upon himself one-sixtieth of the sick person's illness. The ability to do this arises from the unity that exists among the Jewish people. Now, Korach sowed strife and dissension among Jews, but he maintained the public persona of someone who honored Jewish unity. Moses wished to reveal Korach's true colors. He therefore told the Jewish people as follows: If Korach and his men die a natural death prior to which people come to visit him, then this indicates that Korach was indeed concerned about unity and he deserves a display of unity toward himself. But if Korach dies in a sudden catastrophe, such that no one has the opportunity to visit him, this indicates that Korach is not worthy of such displays and his intentions were indeed to foment controversy.

[To elaborate further: A person's attitude to his fellow man is reflected back in that man's attitude to him (see *Proverbs* 27:19). A person who is angry at someone will eventually be the recipient of that person's anger, and one who is warm-hearted to another will enjoy that other's warm-heartedness. If Korach truly cared about the communal welfare and did what he did out of his love for the Jewish people, then there had to have been a reciprocal love from the community; God would not prevent this love from being expressed to Korach. Thus if Korach had to die, he would first become ill, allowing others to visit him. But if in truth Korach was pursuing his selfish interests and to do so he was willing to create controversy, then there would be no reciprocal affection or concern toward him, and there would be no impetus to visit him before his death. Thus, it would be appropriate for Korach to die suddenly, without well-wishers, and this would demonstrate what he really was.]

6. If the people see that Moses' prophecy of catastrophic destruction does not come true, they will then conclude that Moses is not an agent of God. ("People" here refers either to the general populace, the followers of Korach or the well-wishers who will visit them.) However, according to the Midrash (*Bamidbar Rabbah* 18:13) [and the plain meaning of the verse,] it is Moses who will say, God did not send me. That is, it is so certain that the earth will open up etc., that if it does not, Moses says, even he will concede that God did not send him.

דָרַשׁ רָבָא – **Rava expounded:** "אִם־בְּרִיאָה יִבְרָא ה׳ " – Moses continued:[7] *But if a creation Hashem will create, and the earth opens its mouth and swallows them and all that is theirs, and they will descend alive to the pit – then you shall know that these men have provoked Hashem!*[8] The beginning of this verse should be understood as follows: אִם בְּרִיאָה גֵּיהִנֹם – *If* **Gehinnom** (Purgatory) **is a creation,** i.e. if God has already created Gehinnom, מוּטָב תִּהְיֶה – then **that will be fine.** It will be available to swallow up Korach's faction. אִם לָאו – **But if** Gehinnom has **not** been created yet, יִבְרָא ה׳ – *let Hashem create* it now!

The Gemara cites a ruling in regard to visiting the sick:

תַּנְיָא – **It has been taught in a Baraisa:** בִּיקוּר חוֹלִים אֵין לָה שִׁיעוּר – VISITING THE SICK is a mitzvah that HAS NO LIMIT.

The Gemara analyzes this statement:

סָבַר רַב – **What** does the Baraisa **mean** that "it has no limit"? מַאי אֵין לָה שִׁיעוּר יוֹסֵף לְמֵימַר – **Rav Yosef thought to say** it means אֵין שִׁיעוּר לְמַתַּן שְׂכָרָה – **there is no limit to the reward** that Heaven will bestow upon someone who visits the sick. אָמַר לֵיהּ אַבַּיֵּי – **Abaye said to him:** וְכָל מִצְוֹת מִי יֵשׁ שִׁיעוּר לְמַתַּן שְׂכָרָן – **And in regard to all other mitzvos is there** then **a limit to their reward** of which we are aware? Certainly not, because God withheld this information, וְהָא תְּנַן – **for we have learned in the Mishnah:**[9] הֱוֵי זָהִיר בְּמִצְוָה קַלָּה כְּבַחֲמוּרָה – **Be as scrupulous in regard to the performance of a "minor" mitzvah as you would be in regard to the performance of a "major" mitzvah,** שֶׁאֵין אַתָּה יוֹדֵעַ מַתַּן שְׂכָרָן שֶׁל מִצְוֹת – **for you do not know the reward bestowed for** the respective **mitzvos.**[10]

NOTES

7. *Numbers* 16:30.

8. The usual translation of this phrase would be: *But if God will create a phenomenon.* Rava, however, is bothered by the apparent incongruity of the literal meaning: *But if a creation* implies there is already a creation and *Hashem will create* implies that Hashem will have to create it.

9. *Avos* 2:1.

10. We generally do not know if a particular positive commandment is more important or less important than others. God hid the relative value of these mitzvos on purpose so that none of them should go unfulfilled. The Midrash (*Devarim Rabbah* 6:2) offers the parable of a king who commanded his servants to tend to his orchard. If he were to tell them that a certain tree is very valuable and the work on that tree will be rewarded more generously than that of another, less valuable tree, all the servants would abandon the lesser trees in order to increase their earnings. However, if the king were to command them to work in the orchard without disclosing the value of each tree, the entire orchard would receive the same care. Similarly, if God were to reveal which positive commandments are the most precious, people would be inclined to ignore the rest (*Rashi* and *Rabbeinu Yonah* to *Avos* 2:1).

[Since God concealed the rewards of mitzvos intentionally, so that we should not focus on one at the expense of others, how could our Baraisa tell us that one mitzvah (visiting the sick) is rewarded more than others? This defeats the entire purpose of the concealment!]

It should be noted that at least according to *Rambam* [to *Pirkei Avos* 2:1] there are

The Gemara offers another interpretation:

אֶלָּא אָמַר אַבֵּיי – **Rather Abaye said:** *"It has no limit"* means that אֲפִילוּ גָדוֹל אֵצֶל קָטָן – **even a great person** must visit **a lesser person** who is ill. There is no limit to the disparity between the status of the visitor and the status of the sick person.[11]

Another explanation:

רָבָא אָמַר – **Rava said:** There is no limit in regard to how often one should visit the sick, אֲפִילוּ מֵאָה פְּעָמִים בַּיּוֹם – **even one hundred times a day,** as long as one does not inconvenience the sick person.[12]

The Gemara cites another statement regarding the importance of visiting the sick:

אָמַר רַבִּי אַחָא בַּר חֲנִינָא – **R' Acha bar Chanina said:** כָּל הַמְבַקֵּר חוֹלֶה – **Whoever visits a sick person** נוֹטֵל אֶחָד מִשִּׁשִּׁים בְּצַעֲרוֹ – **takes away one-sixtieth of his suffering.**[13]

NOTES

some positive commandments that the Torah *does* indicate as being more important than others, such as circumcision and the bringing of the *pesach* offering. [However, where the Torah does not indicate the importance of a mitzvah clearly, it seems unlikely that a Baraisa would do so.]

11. It is a truism that people separate naturally into social classes. Distinguished men associate with other distinguished men and visit one another while simple folk befriend other simple folk and visit among themselves. Generally speaking, it would impinge upon the dignity of an esteemed personage to have to visit and socialize with "the masses." And we find, for example, that where such a person's dignity would be violated, he is exempt from returning a lost object (*Bava Metzia* 30a).

However, there is no such exemption in regard to visiting the sick (*Shitah Mekubetzes*). Concerning this mitzvah, the Sages taught us that all societal limits and boundaries are meaningless. *The mitzvah of visiting the sick is incumbent upon everyone, even a great person must visit a lesser person* (*Rambam, Hil. Aveil* 14:4). A person should not say, "I will visit only a great person, like myself," because it is a mitzvah to visit a lesser person just as it is a mitzvah to visit a greater person (*Mefaresh*).

12. *Rambam* loc. cit.; see *Beis Yosef, Yoreh Deah* 335 ד״ה ומ״ש וכל המוסיף.

[It has been remarked that it is possible to fulfill the mitzvah of visiting the sick even with a very short visit. One may calculate that if one were to visit a hundred times during the permitted visiting hours (see below, 40a) then each visit would be but a few minutes (see related points in *Meiri* and *Tzitz Eliezer,* vol. V, *Ramat Rachel* 8:3-4). In any case, one should not impose upon the ailing by visiting too long; *Meiri* states among a series of aphorisms: A main objective of the visit is not to tarry (*Chibbur HaTeshuvah* II 2:9).]

In the version of our text found in *Ein Yaakov,* the Gemara cites a Baraisa that teaches both Abaye's and Rava's explanations of "no limit." Both explanations are followed in halachah (see *Yoreh Deah* 335:2).

13. The sick person's enjoyment of the visitor's pleasant company improves his condition (*Meiri, Shitah Mekubetzes*).

The Gemara in *Bava Metzia* 30b implies that the visitor takes this sixtieth upon himself and despite the suffering he will undergo, he must still visit the sick person (see also *Tur* and *Shulchan Aruch, Yoreh Deah* 335:2). [In the context of the *Meiri's* explanation, it would seem that the Gemara means a person cannot refuse to visit a sick person simply because it would pain him to see his colleague suffering.]

The Gemara notes an objection:

אָמְרִי לֵיהּ – **They said to [R' Acha bar Chanina]:** אִם כֵּן לִיעֲלוּן שִׁיתִּין וְלוֹקְמוּהּ – **If so,** we have an easy way to cure any sick person: **Sixty people should go in** to visit him **and restore him** to health.

The Gemara answers:

אָמַר לֵיהּ – **[R' Acha bar Chanina] said to them:** Those "one-sixtieths" follow the same pattern כְּעִישׂוּרַיְיתָא דְּבֵי רַבִּי – **as the "tenths" of the academy of Rebbe.** That is, each visitor takes one-sixtieth of what his predecessor has left.[14] וּבְבֶן גִּילוֹ – **Also,** the capacity to take away suffering is possessed only **by a "ben gilo."**[15]

The Gemara cites a Baraisa to explain what is meant by "the tenths of Rebbi":

דְּתַנְיָא – **For it has been taught in a Baraisa:** בַּת – רַבִּי אוֹמֵר – REBBI SAID: הַנִּיזוֹנֵית מִנִּכְסֵי אַחִין – A DAUGHTER WHO IS BEING SUPPORTED BY the estate inherited by THE BROTHERS[16] נוֹטֶלֶת עִישׂוּר נְכָסִים – TAKES A TENTH OF THE ESTATE for her dowry when she marries.[17] אָמְרוּ לוֹ לְרַבִּי – THEY SAID TO REBBI: לִדְבָרֶיךָ – ACCORDING TO YOUR WORDS, מִי שֶׁיֵּשׁ לוֹ עֶשֶׂר בָּנוֹת וּבֵן – IF ONE HAS TEN DAUGHTERS AND A SON, אֵין לוֹ לַבֵּן בִּמְקוֹם בָּנוֹת כְּלוּם – THE SON GETS NOTHING ON ACCOUNT OF THE DAUGHTERS! אָמַר לָהֶן – [REBBI] ANSWERED THEM: This is what I am saying: רִאשׁוֹנָה נוֹטֶלֶת עִישׂוּר נְכָסִים – THE FIRST [daughter] TAKES A TENTH OF THE ESTATE; שְׁנִיָּה בְּמַה שֶּׁשִּׁיְּירָה – THE SECOND takes a tenth OF WHAT [THE FIRST ONE] LEFT; שְׁלִישִׁית בְּמַה שֶּׁשִּׁיְּירָה – THE THIRD takes a tenth OF THAT WHICH [THE SECOND ONE] LEFT, and so on.[18] וְחוֹזְרוֹת וְחוֹלְקוֹת בְּשָׁוֶה – AND THEN

NOTES

14. Thus, sixty visitors will not take away the entire illness. They will, though, take away 63.5 percent of the illness, and 275 visitors would take away more than 99 percent of it. However, as the Gemara notes immediately, there is another condition that makes the appearance of so many cure-assisting visitors unlikely.

15. *Ran* and *Rosh* say that this refers to someone born under the same constellation as the sick person (cf. *Mefaresh*). The *Shitah Mekubetzes* explains that "being born under the same constellation" means he is a kindred spirit: a person whose nature and behavior conform to that of the sick person. Under these circumstances, the pleasantness of such a visit will ameliorate the person's sickness. However, a visitor whose nature and behavior clash with those of the sick person is liable to upset the sick person and make the ailment lie more heavily upon him (see *Shitah Mekubetzes*).

16. There is a standard *kesubah* stipulation that one's daughters should be supported from one's estate after his death until they attain *bagrus* (the final legal stage in a female's development that begins when she is twelve and a half). Thus, the phrase "a daughter who is being supported by the brothers" describes a minor or a *naarah*.

17. [There is a dispute as to whether a daughter still receives a tenth of her father's estate if the court has clear evidence that the father was more generous or less generous (see *Kesubos* 68a; *Shitah MeKubetzes* ad loc. סד״ה אלא שמין in explanation of *Rashi;* cf. *Ran* there).]

18. The first daughter takes 10 percent of the estate, leaving 90 percent. The second takes a tenth of the remaining 90 percent, which is 9 percent, leaving 81 percent. The third takes a tenth of 81 percent which is 8.1 percent. The next seven daughters take (approximately) the following percentages: 7.3, 6.6, 5.9, 5.3, 4.8, 4.3 and 3.9.

THEY ALL SHARE the portions EQUALLY.[19]

The Gemara cites an incident in regard to visiting the sick and the responsibilities of a visitor:

רַב חֶלְבּוֹ חָלַשׁ – **Rav Chelbo took ill.** נָפַק אַכְרִיז רַב כַּהֲנָא – **Rav Kahana went out and proclaimed to** the public:

NOTES

19. The ten shares are pooled together, for a total of approximately 65 percent. This total is then divided equally among the ten daughters, each receiving approximately 6.5 percent.

[This procedure is followed only if all the ten daughters marry at the same time. If they get married one after the other, then each daughter is given a tenth of the entire estate extant at the time of her marriage, whatever its current value.]

Nedarim 40a

לֹא רַב חֶלְבּוֹ בָּאִישׁ – **"Rav Chelbo has taken ill! Rav Chelbo has taken ill!"**[1] אָמַר לְהוּ – אִיכָּא דְּקָא אָתֵי – **Nevertheless, no one came** to visit him. [Rav Kahana] **said to [the people],** לֹא כָּךְ הָיָה מַעֲשֶׂה – **"Is this not the same story** that took place בְּתַלְמִיד אֶחָד מִתַּלְמִידֵי רַבִּי עֲקִיבָא – **with one student from among R' Akiva's students?** שֶׁחָלָה – **For he took ill,** לֹא נִכְנְסוּ חֲכָמִים לְבַקְּרוֹ – and **none of the Sages went in to visit him**[2] וְנִכְנַס רַבִּי עֲקִיבָא לְבַקְּרוֹ – **until, finally, R' Akiva went in to visit him.** וּבִשְׁבִיל שֶׁכִּיבְּדוּ וְרִיבְּצוּ לְפָנָיו חָיָה – **And because they swept** the floor **and settled the dust** on the ground **before him, he became better.**[3] אָמַר לוֹ – **[The student] said to [R' Akiva],** רַבִּי הֶחֱיֵיתָנִי **'My teacher, you have brought me back to life!'** יָצָא רַבִּי עֲקִיבָא וְדָרַשׁ – **R' Akiva emerged and expounded** to the public: כָּל מִי שֶׁאֵין מְבַקֵּר חוֹלִים – **Whoever does not visit the sick** כְּאִילּוּ שׁוֹפֵךְ דָּמִים – **is as if he spills blood."**[4]

The Gemara presents a related teaching:

כִּי אֲתָא רַב דִּימִי אָמַר – **When Rav Dimi came** from Eretz Yisrael to Babylonia,[5] **he said:** כָּל הַמְבַקֵּר אֶת הַחוֹלֶה גּוֹרֵם לוֹ שֶׁיִּחְיֶה – **Whoever visits the sick, causes [the sick person] to live,** וְכָל שֶׁאֵינוֹ מְבַקֵּר אֶת הַחוֹלֶה גּוֹרֵם לוֹ שֶׁיָּמוּת – **and whoever does not visit the sick, causes [the sick person] to die.**

The Gemara analyzes this teaching:

NOTES

1. [See version of our text in *Ein Yaakov*.] The word בָּאִישׁ means "is in a bad way" and is used in reference to a sick person (see *Rosh* here and *Rashi* to *Shabbos* 30a ד"ה באישא), possibly a person who is critically ill (see *Shabbos* loc. cit.).

2. [See *Shalmei Nedarim* who offers a theory as to why the Sages did not visit this student or R' Chelbo.]

3. The *Shitah Mekubetzes* explains: R' Akiva saw that the room where the ailing student lay was dirty and dusty, and that this had a detrimental effect upon the student's well-being. He therefore directed the members of the household to sweep the room and to sprinkle some water on the dirt floor in order to settle the dust. *Rosh* notes that this is what a visitor to a sick person is supposed to do: to check on the sick person's needs and make sure that they are satisfied.

According to another version of our text, R' Akiva *himself* swept the floor for the student's benefit (*Kol Bo* 112 and *Menoras HaMaor* 207). According to other sources, the household members swept the floor in honor of R' Akiva (*Meiri*, second explanation) or the housekeeper saw how esteemed the student was in R' Akiva's eyes and therefore attended to the student's needs for the student's sake (*She'iltos, Acharei Mos* 93).

4. There are times when the failure to visit a sick person and attend to his needs could lead to his death (see *Mefaresh, Meiri*).

5. Rav Dimi was one of a group of Sages who would ascend to Eretz Yisrael to learn Torah and return to Babylonia with halachic and Aggadic teachings learned from the masters in Eretz Yisrael. They were called *nachosei* – those who descend (see *Succah* 43b with *Rashi* ד"ה וכל נחותי). This group included some Sages who were originally from Eretz Yisrael (*Rashi* ibid.); however, Rav Dimi himself was a Babylonian (see *Temurah* 12a and *Iggeres Rav Sherira Gaon,* R' N. D. Rabinowich ed., Ch. 8).

מַאי גְּרְמָא – In **what** way does the visitor **cause** the sick person to live or die?[6]

אִילֵּימָא כָּל הַמְּבַקֵּר אֶת הַחוֹלֶה – **If you will say** that Rav Dimi means **whoever visits a sick person** is presumably one of his friends and מְבַקֵּשׁ עָלָיו רַחֲמִים שֶׁיִּחְיֶה – **will supplicate** God **for mercy that he live,** וְכָל שֶׁאֵין מְבַקֵּר אֶת הַחוֹלֶה – **but** whoever does not visit a sick person is presumably among his detractors and מְבַקֵּשׁ עָלָיו רַחֲמִים שֶׁיָּמוּת – **will supplicate** God for **"mercy" that he die,** that is an unlikely interpretation: For even if someone is a detractor and therefore will not visit the sick person, but שָׁיָמוּת סָלְקָא דַּעְתָּךְ – **could you** possibly **think** that his lack of affection would lead him to pray **that [the sick person] die?!**[7]

The Gemara revises its interpretation:

אֶלָּא כָּל שֶׁאֵין מְבַקֵּר חוֹלֶה אֵין מְבַקֵּשׁ עָלָיו רַחֲמִים – **Rather,** Rav Dimi means as follows: **Whoever does not visit a sick person will not pray for** God's **mercies** concerning him at all. לֹא שֶׁיִּחְיֶה וְלֹא שֶׁיָּמוּת – He will **not** pray **that he should live,** because he is unaware of the state of his health,[8] and he will certainly **not** pray **that he will die.** Because he does not pray at all, he can cause the sick person to die, since if he had prayed and it was a propitious moment, his prayer would have been accepted and the sick person would have been spared death.[9]

The practice of an Amora in regard to publicizing his episodes of illness:

רָבָא יוֹמָא קַדְמָאָה דַּחֲלִישׁ – **On the first day that Rava would take ill,** אָמַר לְהוּ – he would tell [the people in his household], לֹא תִּיגְלוּ לְאִינִישׁ – **"Do not reveal** my condition **to any person."** דְּלָא לְתְרַע מַזָּלֵיהּ – He kept his condition a secret in the hope **that his luck would not worsen.**[10] מִכָּאן וְאֵילָךְ אָמַר לְהוּ – However,

---

NOTES

6. [The Gemara assumes that Rav Dimi is *not* speaking in reference to the same situation that R' Akiva dealt with above (i.e. a sick person whose therapeutic needs are not being satisfied). See *Maharsha* and *Eitz Yosef* who discuss this point. (See also the version of our text in *Ein Yaakov.*)]

7. *Maharsha.*

8. *Mefaresh.*

9. *Rosh.*

Ran explains the Gemara's discussion somewhat differently; however, as *Maharsha* points out, his explanation does not seem to conform to the words of our text. [Possibly, *Ran* had the version of our text that appears in *Ein Yaakov,* in which the Gemara revises, and not merely reinterprets, Rav Dimi's original statement.]

According to *Ran,* our Gemara's conclusion indicates that it is sometimes proper for a person to pray that a sick person should die, i.e. in a case where there is no hope for recovery and death would end his terrible suffering. *Ran* cites an example of this principle from *Kesubos* 104a where it is related that Rebbi was very ill and in great pain and his maidservant prayed that the Heavenly forces should vanquish the earthly forces and take his soul. See discussion of this point and related issues in *Responsa, Chikekei Lev* I *Yoreh Deah* 50, *Igros Moshe, Choshen Mishpat* II 73-74; and *Tzitz Eliezer,* V *Ramat Rachel* 5.

10. [At the very onset of illness, it is possible that a person's fortunes will be reversed and he will return quickly to health, and it is also possible that he will become much sicker. At this point, he is in a precarious position in Heaven's scales of justice and the disclosure of his condition could tip those scales against him (see *Rosh*).] There are different explanations as to how this works (although the differences between them may

from then on, if his illness persisted, **he would tell them,** פּוּקוּ וְאַכְרִיזוּ בְשׁוּקָא – "**Go out and announce in the marketplace** that I have taken ill.[11] This will be advantageous to me no matter who hears of my sickness: דְּכָל דְּסָנֵי לִי לִיחְדֵי לִי – **For whoever dislikes me will take joy over me** and my predicament, וּכְתִיב – **and it is written:**[12] "בִּנְפֹל אוֹיִבְךָ אַל־תִּשְׂמָח וגו' " – **When your foe falls, be not glad etc.,** *and when he stumbles, let your heart not be joyous; lest Hashem see and it be displeasing in His eyes, and He turn His anger from him.* Thus, his joy over my troubles will be beneficial to me.[13] וּדְרָחִים לִי לִבְעֵי עֲלַי רַחֲמֵי – **And whoever likes me will supplicate** God **for mercy on my behalf."**

Another teaching in regard to the benefit of visiting the sick:

אָמַר רַב – **Rav said:** כָּל הַמְבַקֵּר אֶת הַחוֹלֶה נִיצוֹל מִדִּינָה שֶׁל גֵּיהִנֹּם – **Whoever visits the sick is spared from the judgment of Gehinnom,** שֶׁנֶּאֱמַר – **as it says:**[14] "אַשְׁרֵי מַשְׂכִּיל אֶל־דָּל בְּיוֹם רָעָה יְמַלְּטֵהוּ ה' " – *Praiseworthy is he who contemplates the needy* (*dal*), *on the day of evil Hashem will deliver him.* אֵין דַּל אֶלָּא חוֹלֶה – **And the word** *dal* **refers to none other than a sick person, as it says:**[15] "מִדַּלָּה יְבַצְּעֵנִי" – *He will end* [*my life*] *with sickness* (*midalah*).[16] אִי

NOTES

be semantic): (a) *Shitah Mekubetzes* writes that everyone has his enemies. When these enemies hear of his illness, they will say that he deserves what he is suffering because of this sin and that fault. There is a possibility that Above they will judge him as he has been judged by these detractors below, and his illness will be prolonged. (b) *Maharsha* points out that בְּרִית כְּרוּתָה לַשְּׂפָתַיִם, *a covenant has been made with the lips* (*Moed Katan* 18a). That is, a man's words may inadvertently contain some prophecy of the future (see *Maharsha* ad loc.). [The very mention by people that Rava is ill may be akin to a self-fulfilling prophecy.] (c) Along these lines, another Gemara comments (*Berachos* 19a): לְעוֹלָם אַל יִפְתַּח אָדָם פִּיו לַשָּׂטָן, *one ought not give Satan an opening.* Typically, this means that one ought not speak of punishments he believes he might deserve, for by doing so he gives Satan (who functions as the prosecutor in the Heavenly Tribunal) an opening to demand that he be punished as he has spoken. In our context, this principle is extended: Rava did not want people speaking vividly of the hardship that befell him, lest this, too, strengthen Satan's hand against him (see *Maharsha* to *Berachos* 55b).

11. By the second day of his illness, it would be clear that his fortunes had already taken a turn for the worse, and he was lacking prayer on his behalf (see *Shitah Mekubetzes*).

12. *Proverbs* 24:17-18.

13. Having one's enemies gloating over one's tribulations is itself an intense tribulation. This in turn may lead the Heavenly Tribunal to decide that the sick person has been afflicted greatly already and need be afflicted no more. The Tribunal may then decide that the gloater's failure to observe the commandment (*Leviticus* 19:17), *Do not hate your brother in your heart,* is sufficient cause to transfer the misfortune from the sick person to him (*Shitah Mekubetzes*).

14. *Psalms* 41:2.

15. *Isaiah* 38:12.

16. This part of a verse appears in a prayer composed by King Hezekiah after he recuperated from an illness that nearly took his life (see *Isaiah* Ch. 38). The word דָּל usually refers to someone who is needy in an economic sense, not in a medical sense. However, in the context of Hezekiah's supplication it is clear that the word refers to ill health and not poverty (see *Maharsha*).

נַמֵּי מִן הָדֵין קְרָא – **Or else,** prove that *dal* refers to a sick person **from this verse:**[17] " מַדּוּעַ אַתָּה כָּכָה דַּל בֶּן־הַמֶּלֶךְ בַּבֹּקֶר בַּבֹּקֶר וְגוֹ' " – *Why are you so sickly, (dal) son of the king, morning after morning?* **etc.**[18] אֵין רָעָה אֶלָּא גֵּיהִנֹּם שֶׁנֶּאֱמַר – And the word **evil refers to none other than Gehinnom, as it says:**[19] " כֹּל פָּעַל ה' לַמַעֲנֵהוּ וְגַם־רָשָׁע לְיוֹם רָעָה" – *Everything Hashem made [He made] for His praise, even the wicked man for the day of evil,* i.e. even when a wicked man is punished in Gehinnom, this contributes to God's praise.[20] In any case, we have demonstrated that the first verse should read: *Praiseworthy is he who contemplates the sick person, on the day of Gehinnom, Hashem will deliver him.*[21]

Rav continues his teaching:

וְאִם בִּיקֵּר מַה שְּׂכָרוֹ – **And if someone does visit** the sick, **what is his reward?**

The Gemara interrupts to ask:

מַה שְּׂכָרוֹ – **What is his reward?!** כִּדְאָמַר – His reward is as [Rav] said before: נִיצוֹל מִדִּינָהּ שֶׁל גֵּיהִנֹּם – **He is spared from the judgment of Gehinnom!**

The Gemara explains and continues with Rav's teaching:

אֶלָּא מַה שְּׂכָרוֹ בָּעוֹלָם הַזֶּה – **Rather,** Rav means to ask, **what is his reward in this world?**[22] "ה' יִשְׁמְרֵהוּ וִיחַיֵּהוּ וְאֻשַּׁר בָּאָרֶץ" – *Hashem will guard him and restore*

NOTES

17. *II Samuel* 13:4.

18. The passage speaks about King David's son Amnon who lusted after his half-sister Tamar until he made himself ill. At that point, his friend Yonadav addressed to him the question cited in our Gemara. *Why are you so sickly, O son of the king?* (see *II Samuel* 13:1-22).

The *Netziv* explains the import of each verse in regard to the mitzvah of visiting the sick: The verse spoken by Hezekiah teaches us regarding the visit of a critically ill person, whereas the verse spoken to Amnon teaches us regarding the visit of a mildly ill person (see *Haamek She'eilah, Acharei Mos* 93:8).

19. *Proverbs* 16:4.

20. Every thing and every action in this world contribute to God's greater glory. Among humans, who have free will, it is not only the righteous person who obeys God's mitzvos who furthers God's praise, but even the wicked man who violates God's commandments furthers His praise (albeit involuntarily) when he is punished for his sins. A person's choice is only whether to contribute to God's praise actively or by being an example (*Maharal, Derech Chaim,* end of Ch. 6; *Sifsei Chaim, Mo'adim* II pp. 252-253).

[In this verse, *the day of evil* refers to the day the wicked person is judged and ordered into Gehinnom. In the verse, *Praiseworthy is he who contemplates . . . on the day of evil, Hashem will deliver him,* the phrase *day of evil* has the same meaning (see *Eitz Yosef*).]

21. *Geon Yaakov* comments: Visiting the sick produces two benefits: one for the visitor and one for the visited. The benefit for the visitor is the moral lesson he should draw from coming face-to-face with serious illness. This is the message of our verse: *Praiseworthy is he who contemplates the sick person.* The visitor must contemplate carefully the spiritual causes of illness and suffering; he must observe the therapeutic procedures carried out to improve the sick person's health and take to heart the analogies to treatments for spiritual malaise. If he does so, he will certainly merit to repent sincerely and he will thereby be spared the punishment of Gehinnom.

22. What is his reward for the benefit he imparts to the sick person who is visited? It stands to reason that since he attended to the sick person's worldly needs, he should be

him to life and he will be fortunate on earth – "וְאַל־תִּתְּנֵהוּ בְּנֶפֶשׁ אֹיְבָיו"
will not give him over to the desire of his foes.[23] – "ה' יִשְׁמְרֵהוּ" מִיֵּצֶר הָרַע
Hashem will guard him from the Evil Inclination; "וִיחַיֵּהוּ" מִן הַיִּסּוּרִין – *and*
restore him to life from his suffering; "וְאֻשַּׁר בָּאָרֶץ" שֶׁיְהֵא הַכֹּל מִתְכַּבְּדִין בּוֹ – *and*
he will be fortunate on earth in that everyone will take pride in him; "וְאַל־
תִּתְּנֵהוּ בְּנֶפֶשׁ אֹיְבָיו" – *and You will not give him over to the desire of his foes,*
כְּנַעֲמָן שֶׁרִיפּוּ שֶׁיִּזְדַּמְּנוּ לוֹ רֵיעִים – in that he will have available good **friends**[24]
אֶת צָרַעְתּוֹ – such as those that **Naaman** had, who healed his skin disease,[25]
כִּרְחַבְעָם שֶׁחִילְקוּ וְאַל יִזְדַּמְּנוּ לוֹ רֵיעִים – and he will not have available bad **friends**
אֶת מַלְכוּתוֹ – such as those **Rechavam** had, who split his kingdom.[26]

The Gemara cites a Baraisa related to the last part of Rav's teaching:

תַּנְיָא – **It has been taught in a Baraisa:** רַבִּי שִׁמְעוֹן בֶּן אֶלְעָזָר אוֹמֵר – **R' SHIMON BEN ELAZAR SAYS:** אִם יֹאמְרוּ לְךָ יְלָדִים בְּנֵה – **IF YOUTHS TELL YOU, "BUILD,"** וּזְקֵנִים – **AND ELDERS** tell you, "DEMOLISH," סְתוֹר – שְׁמַע לַזְּקֵנִים וְאַל תִּשְׁמַע לַיְלָדִים – **LISTEN TO THE ELDERS AND DO NOT LISTEN TO THE YOUTHS,** שֶׁבִּנְיָן יְלָדִים סְתִירָה – **BECAUSE** THE "BUILDING" OF YOUTHS IS really DEMOLISHING, i.e. it is detrimental, וּסְתִירַת זְקֵנִים בִּנְיָן – AND THE "DESTRUCTION" OF ELDERS IS really BUILDING, i.e. it is beneficial,[27] וְסִימָן לַדָּבָר – AND THE MODEL FOR THIS PRINCIPLE רְחַבְעָם בֶּן

NOTES

King Rechavam took counsel with the elders, who had stood before his father Solomon while he was alive, saying, "How do you advise; what word to respond to this people?"

They spoke to him saying, "If today you become a servant to this people and serve them and respond [favorably] to them and speak kind words to them, they will be your servants all the days."

But he ignored the advice of the elders who had counseled him, and he took counsel with the youths who had grown up with him, who ministered before him. He said to them, "What do you advise; what word shall we respond to this people who have spoken to me, saying, 'Alleviate the yoke that your father placed upon us'?"

The young men who had grown up with him spoke to him saying, "This is what you should say to this people ... 'My little finger is thicker than my father's waist! So now, my father saddled you with a heavy yoke; I shall add to your yoke! My father chastised you with sticks; I shall chastise you with scorpions!' "

Yarovam and all the people came to Rechavam on the third day ... The king responded harshly to the people; he ignored the advice of the elders who had counseled him. He spoke to them according to the counsel of the youths ...

All of Israel saw that the king did not listen to them, and the people gave their response to the king, saying, "What share have we in the [House of] David" ... And [the men of] Israel left for home. As for the Children of Israel who lived in the cities of Judah — Rechavam ruled over them.

King Rechavam dispatched Adoram, who was in charge of the tax — and all of Israel pelted him with stones, and he died. King Rechavam then hastened to mount his chariot to flee to Jerusalem. Thus Israel rebelled against the House of David, to this day.

Ben Yehoyada notes a parallel between Naaman and Rechavam. Each had an inclination toward pride and self-importance. In Naaman's case, this was the ultimate cause of his *tzaraas* (see *II Chronicles* 26:18-19 and *Arachin* 16a). Naaman's friends advised him to humble himself by following Elisha's instructions (or by appearing before Elisha in the first place — see *Ben Yehoyada*). He did and he was cured. Rechavam's friends advised him to speak to the people arrogantly, reinforcing his self-importance. He did and his kingdom was torn asunder.

27. Although it is often the proper course to go out and accomplish something rather than to dismantle what has already been achieved, nevertheless if the persons advising one to do something constructive are youths and the persons advising one to take a step backward are elders, one should listen to the elders and disregard the youths. This is because the advice of youths is the product of inexperience and restlessness, whereas the advice of elders is the product of composed minds and lifetimes of practical knowledge. One may rest assured that, at least in the long term, the elders' plan will prove more effective than that of the youths.

The *Tosefta* (*Avodah Zarah* 1:19) states the point more dramatically: *If youths tell you to build the Temple and elders tell you to destroy it, you should destroy it and not build it.*

שְׁלֹמֹה – IS the incident that occurred with RECHAVAM THE SON OF SOLOMON.[28]

The Gemara returns to the subject of visiting the sick:

אָמַר רַב שִׁישָׁא בְּרֵיהּ דְּרַב אִידִי – Rav Shisha the son of Rav Idi said: לֹא לִיסְעוֹד – not לֹא בִּתְלָת שָׁעֵי קַדְמָיָיתָא – One should not visit a sick person, in the first three hours of the daytime וְלֹא בִּתְלָת שָׁעֵי בַּתְרָיָיתָא דְּיוֹמָא – nor in the last three hours of the daytime.[29] The reason is כִּי הֵיכִי דְּלָא לִיסַּח דַּעְתֵּיהּ מִן רַחֲמֵי – so that [the visitor] should not give up on praying for God's mercies. תְּלָת שָׁעֵי קַדְמָיָיתָא רְוַוחָא דַעְתֵּיהּ – In the first three hours, [a sick person's] mind is at ease,[30] and consequently the visitor might think it unnecessary to pray for him. בַּתְרָיָיתָא תָּקִיף חוּלְשֵׁיהּ – In the last three hours, the illness becomes more intense, and the visitor may think the situation hopeless.[31]

The Gemara discusses the special providence merited by a sick person:

אָמַר רָבִין אָמַר רַב – Ravin said in the name of Rav: מִנַּיִן שֶׁהַקָּדוֹשׁ בָּרוּךְ הוּא זָן אֶת הַחוֹלֶה – From where do we know that the Holy One, Blessed is He, sustains a sick person? שֶׁנֶּאֱמַר – As it says, "ה׳ יִסְעָדֶנּוּ עַל־עֶרֶשׂ דְּוָי וגו׳ " – Hashem will

---

NOTES

28. [See note 26.] It should be noted that Rechavam was forty-one years old when he began his reign (I Kings 14:21) and so his peers, the advisers with whom he grew up, were hardly youngsters. However, in relation to the elders, who had stood before his father Solomon, they were considered immature youths.

The advice of the youths resulted in a divided people, ongoing wars between the two kingdoms of Judah and Israel, the spilling of much blood, the disallowance of pilgrimages to the Temple, and eventually the exile of the Ten Tribes, the destruction of the Temple and the expulsion of the rest of the Jewish people from their land (see Ben Yehoyada and Or Yeshuah).

29. These are probably seasonal hours שָׁעוֹת זְמַנִּיוֹת: (Ahavas Chesed 3:3): That is, each hour is one-twelfth of the time between sunrise and sunset (or between dawn's first light and nightfall). Thus, if the daytime is nine hours long (such as it is sometimes in the winter), a seasonal hour is 45 minutes; and if the daytime is fifteen hours long (as it is sometimes in the summer) a seasonal hour is 75 minutes long. In the first case, three seasonal hours are 2 hours and 15 minutes; in the second, three seasonal hours are 3 hours and 45 minutes.

30. In general, a sick person feels better in the morning (see Bava Basra 16b, cited by Mefaresh; see also Rashi ad loc. ד"ה אידלי קצירא).

31. Rambam (Hil. Aveil 14:5) writes a different reason to avoid visiting at these times: These are the times that the physician is attending to the patient. Kesef Mishneh ad loc. wonders why Rambam ignores the reason mentioned in our Gemara and therefore suggests that Rambam may have had a version of our text that omits this line. Indeed, Dikdukei Soferim HaShalem reports that there are many manuscripts of our Gemara that omit the words כִּי הֵיכִי דְּלָא לִיסַּח דַּעְתֵּיהּ מִן רַחֲמֵי, so that he should not give up on [praying for mercy]. Radvaz ad loc. comments that Rambam supplied his own reason based on his medical expertise (see Birkei Yosef, Yoreh Deah 335:2).

Yerushalmi (Pe'ah 3:9) teaches a related ruling that is cited in various halachic works: A person should not visit someone who has taken ill until the third day of his illness (so that the visitor not worry the sick person unnecessarily regarding the gravity of his situation – Meiri). If however a person is a relative, or a close friend, or if a grave illness fell suddenly upon the sick person and there is a concern that he might die soon, it is permitted to visit right away.

fortify him on the sickbed etc.[32]

Another exposition of these Amoraim on this verse:

מִנַּיִן שֶׁהַשְּׁכִינָה שְׁרוּיָה – **And Ravin said in the name of Rav:** לְמַעְלָה מִמִּטָּתוֹ שֶׁל הַחוֹלֶה – **From where do we know that the Divine Presence rests above the bed of a sick person?** שֶׁנֶּאֱמַר – **As it is stated:** ה׳ יִסְעָדֶנּוּ עַל- "עֶרֶשׂ דְּוָי" – *Hashem will fortify him* [while Hashem is] **on the sickbed.**[33]

The Gemara cites a Baraisa that corroborates this teaching:

– הַנִּכְנָס לְבַקֵּר אֶת הַחוֹלֶה **This has also been taught in a Baraisa:** תַּנְיָא נַמֵּי הָכִי – **ONE WHO GOES IN TO VISIT A SICK PERSON** לֹא יֵשֵׁב לֹא עַל גַּבֵּי מִטָּה – **SHOULD SIT NEITHER UPON THE BED,** וְלֹא עַל גַּבֵּי סַפְסָל וְלֹא עַל גַּבֵּי כִסֵּא – **NOR UPON A BENCH NOR UPON A CHAIR;**[34] אֶלָּא מִתְעַטֵּף וְיוֹשֵׁב עַל גַּבֵּי קַרְקַע – **RATHER HE SHOULD WRAP HIMSELF** in his cloak[35] **AND SIT UPON THE GROUND,**[36] מִפְּנֵי שֶׁהַשְּׁכִינָה שְׁרוּיָה – **BECAUSE THE DIVINE PRESENCE RESTS ABOVE THE BED OF A SICK PERSON.** לְמַעְלָה מִמִּטָּתוֹ שֶׁל חוֹלֶה – שֶׁנֶּאֱמַר "ה׳ יִסְעָדֶנּוּ עַל-עֶרֶשׂ דְּוָי" – **AS IT SAYS:** *HASHEM WILL FORTIFY HIM* [while Hashem is] **ON THE SICKBED.**[37]

NOTES

32. *Psalms* 41:4. יִסְעָדֶנּוּ is cognate to סְעוּדָה, *meal* (see *Genesis* 18:5 for a similar usage). Here the word is interpreted to mean *He feeds him* [the sick person]. God "feeds" a sick person in that He uses the wondrous workings of the human body to maintain a person's life even when illness has prevented that person from eating for a few days (see *Ritva;* cf. *Maharsha*). [Elsewhere in the Gemara we find the idea of a fever itself sustaining a sick person in lieu of food (see *Yevamos* 71b and *Sanhedrin* 108b).]

In the plain meaning of the verse, the root סעד connotes support or strength (see *Psalms* 92:18), and the verse should be translated, *Hashem will strengthen* [or fortify] *the sick person* [as he lies] *upon the sickbed.*

33. The Divine Presence is as a shade upon his head in order to fortify him (*Eitz Yosef*).

Rashi to *Shabbos* 12b (ד״ה סועד) mentions an alternative version of his text that seems to be relevant here. In this version, the Gemara asks: מִנַּיִן שֶׁשְּׁכִינָה סוֹעֵר אֶת הַחוֹלֶה, *From where do we know that the Divine Presence visits a sick person?* שֶׁנֶּאֱמַר "ה׳ יִסְעָדֶנּוּ, *as it says: Hashem will fortify him (yisadenu) on his sickbed.* עַל-עֶרֶשׂ דְּוָי, אַל תִּקְרֵי יִסְעָדֶנּוּ, *Do not pronounce it "yisadenu"* (fortify him) *but rather "yisarenu"* (visit him). אֶלָּא יְסָעֲרֶנּוּ This version is also cited by *Aruch* (ערך סר״ב). [The word סוֹעֵר, translated here as "visit," derives from the word סָעִיר, which is Aramaic for פָּקַד, which means to inspect or examine (see above, 39b note 6).]

34. This restriction applies only where the sick person is lying on the ground or on a low bed. In such a case, if the visitor were to sit on a chair, he would be "higher" than the Divine Presence, which is at the patient's head (see *Ran; Tosafos* to *Shabbos* 12b ד״ה לא; *Rama* to *Yoreh Deah* 335:2; see *Beis Hillel* loc. cit. and *Aruch HaShulchan* loc. cit. 7).

35. This is a sign of reverence for the Divine Presence. By covering his head he limits his view, and thus he sits in the manner of an awestruck person, who does not glance about (*Rashi* to *Shabbos* 12b ד״ה מתעטף).

36. *Meiri* here and to *Shabbos* 12b explains that when the patient sees his visitor manifesting fear of Heaven, he will be motivated to turn to God in sincere repentance.

However, if the visitor sits in a higher place, a twinge of conceit steals its way into the patient's heart as well and he does not focus on prayer and repentance.

37. In the version of our text in *She'iltos* 93, it says that the Divine Presence rests above the head of the sick person and the Angel of Death rests by his feet. The visitor should therefore sit in the middle (see *Haamek She'eilah* ad loc.).

Nedarim 41a

וְשָׂטִיחַ – **and a mat.**[1]

The Gemara cites a related statement:[2]

„בְּחֹסֶר כֹּל‟ – The Torah states:[3] *Because you did not serve Hashem, your God, amid gladness and goodness of heart, when everything was abundant, so you will serve your enemies whom Hashem will send against you, in hunger, and in thirst, in nakedness and* **without anything.** What do the last words, *without anything,* refer to?[4] אָמַר רַב אַמִי אָמַר רַב – **Rav Ami said in the name of Rav:**[5] The phrase means that a person will have to endure בְּלֹא נֵר וּבְלֹא שֻׁלְחָן – **without a lamp and without a table.**[6]

The Gemara presents alternative views:

רַב חִסְדָּא אָמַר – **Rav Chisda said:** He will have to endure בְּלֹא אִשָּׁה – **without a wife.**[7] רַב שֵׁשֶׁת אָמַר – **Rav Sheishess said:** בְּלֹא שַׁמָּשׁ – **Without an assistant.**[8]

NOTES

1. A leather mat (*Ran*), typically carried by wayfarers (*Tosafos*), upon which one may eat or sleep (*Eichah Rabbah* 1:22; see *Ran* and *Rosh;* see also *Keilim* 24:12 with commentaries).

2. According to several versions of our text (see *Dikdukei Soferim HaShalem*), the following is yet another statement by Ravin (or R' Avin) in the name of Rav. (According to our version of the text, it is the second statement of R' Ami in the name of Rav.) Apart from the Amoraim who uttered them, the previous and following statements are somewhat related in their content as well. The previous statement discussed items that are essential to someone going into exile; the following statements discuss items that are essential to a person in general.

3. *Deuteronomy* 28:47-48 (see *Maharsha*).

4. In the plain meaning of the verse, *without anything* means that they will be missing everything. However, the Gemara notes that the verse lists specifically that there will be hunger, thirst and nakedness, even though food, water and clothing are included in the catch-all phrase *without anything*. Therefore, the Gemara expounds the phrase to instead refer to specific items, items that are essential to all people (*Maharsha*).

5. See above, note 2.

6. The essential furnishings of a person's home (see *II Kings* 4:10 regarding the room set up for Elisha).

[The Gemara above mentioned not a table but rather a leather mat as the surface upon which one eats. This is because that Gemara is speaking of implements that one would carry into exile, and a table is not easily portable. Our verse, containing the words *without anything*, is speaking of misfortunes that will befall the people while they are still in their land and their homes.]

7. The Sages state elsewhere: Any man who remains without a wife remains without joy, without blessing, without goodness, without Torah, without protection [from the Evil Inclination] (*Yevamos* 62b), without assistance, without atonement, without peace, without life (*Bereishis Rabbah* 17:2), and he is not considered to be a [complete] man (*Yevamos* 63a).

8. An assistant is especially necessary amidst the hunger, thirst and lack of clothing (mentioned in the beginning of the verse) to help one attain items [with which to survive] (see *Eitz Yosef*).

רַב נַחְמָן אָמַר – Rav Nachman said: בְּלָא דַעָה – Without understanding.[9]

The Gemara cites the opinion of a Tanna on this question:

תָּנָא – A Baraisa taught: He will have to endure בְּלָא מֶלַח וּבְלָא רְבָב – WITHOUT SALT AND WITHOUT GREASE.[10]

The Gemara before indicated that understanding is one of a person's most essential possessions. The Gemara continues on this theme.

אָמַר אַבַּיֵי – Abaye said: נַקְטִינָן – We have a tradition from our forefathers:[11] אֵין עָנִי אֶלָּא בְּדֵעָה – There is no truly destitute person except he who is impoverished of understanding.[12] בְּמַעֲרָבָא אָמְרֵי – In the West, i.e. in Eretz Yisrael,[13] they said: דְּדָא בֵיה – He who has this (understanding) within him, כּוּלָא בֵיה – has everything within him. דְּלָא דָא בֵיה – He who does not have this within him, מַה בֵיה – what is within him? Nothing. דָא קָנֵי – If he acquires this, מַה חָסַר – what does he lack? דָא לֹא קָנֵי – If he does not acquire this, מַה קָנֵי – what has he acquired?[14]

The Gemara returns to teachings regarding the sick:

אָמַר רַבִּי אֲלֶכְסַנְדְּרִי אָמַר רַבִּי חִיָּיא בַּר אַבָּא – R' Alexandri said in the name of R' Chiya bar Abba: אֵין הַחוֹלֶה עוֹמֵד מֵחָלְיוֹ – A sick person does not emerge from his illness עַד שֶׁמּוֹחֲלִין לוֹ עַל כָּל עֲוֹנוֹתָיו – until he has been forgiven for all of his sins,[15]

NOTES

9. Without one's basic mental faculties. According to Rav Nachman, the ultimate deprivation after one has already suffered hunger, thirst and nakedness will be the loss of one's mind. Such a person is truly without anything (see *Rav Nissim Gaon's Introduction* to his *Sefer HaMafte'ach,* printed at the beginning of the Vilna ed. of *Berachos* and at the end of the *Lev Same'ach* ed. of *Rabbeinu Chananel* to *Berachos*).

10. [He will lack those things that give food any taste.]

11. See *Rashi* to *Eruvin* 5a. The following is something about which there is unanimity (*Rav Nissim Gaon* loc. cit.).

12. The truly indigent person is he who is mentally incompetent: He has lost the faculty that distinguishes humans from animals (*Rav Nissim Gaon* loc. cit.; see *Maharsha,* second explanation).

13. [Eretz Yisrael lies to the west from the perspective of someone in Babylonia.]

14. It would seem at first that this well-known saying is repetitive (He who has this/if he acquires this; he who does not have this/if he does not acquire this). However, *Eitz Yosef* explains that the two halves of the aphorism pertain to different kinds of people: those who are born with intelligence and those who are not. Among those who are not, there are some who labor to acquire understanding and there are some who remain with their natural slow-wittedness. The aphorism thus means: He who has this within him (inborn within him) has everything within him . . . If (he has no inborn intelligence but) he acquires this, what does he lack? (But) if (he does not have inborn intelligence and) he does not acquire this, what has he acquired?

Ran adds: Of what use is whatever acquisition he may come by in his life if he does not have understanding?

15. When a person is seriously ill, he is called to account for all his faults and imperfections. Any sins that have not yet been atoned for will prevent his immediate recovery, and the suffering warranted by those sins will continue to be extracted from him. Thus, if he does recover, it follows that all his sins must have been forgiven (*Shitah Mekubetzes;* see *Maharsha;* see *Maharal* cited below, note 22).

שֶׁנֶּאֱמַר – **as it says:**[16] **God is He** "הַסֹּלֵחַ לְכָל־עֲוֹנֵכִי הָרֹפֵא לְכָל־תַּחֲלֻאָיְכִי" – **Who forgives all your sins; Who heals all your diseases.** The order of these two clauses teaches us that God forgives the sins of a sick person before He heals him.

A somewhat different statement regarding a sick person who recovers:

חוֹזֵר לִימֵי עֲלוּמָיו – **He returns to the days** רַב הַמְנוּנָא אָמַר – **Rav Hamnuna said: of his youth,** שֶׁנֶּאֱמַר – **as it says:**[17] "רֻטֲפַשׁ בְּשָׂרוֹ מִנֹּעַר" – **His skin will be surpassingly fresh,**[18] **more than in childhood,** "יָשׁוּב לִימֵי עֲלוּמָיו" – **he shall return to the days of his youth.** [19]

The Gemara expounds a verse that alludes to another lasting effect of illness:

"כָּל־מִשְׁכָּבוֹ הָפַכְתָּ בְחָלְיוֹ" – Scripture states:[20] **You have upset all his bedding through his illness.**[21] לוֹמַר דְּמַשְׁכַּח לָמוּדוֹ – **Rav Yosef said:** אָמַר רַב יוֹסֵף The verse means **to say that [the illness] causes** the sick person **to forget** all his **learning,** which is analogous to a well-made bed.[22]

NOTES

16. *Psalms* 103:3.

17. *Job* 33:25. This verse is speaking about someone recovering from a serious illness, as is clear from its context.

18. The unusual word רֻטֲפַשׁ that appears only once in Scripture is a combination of the words רָטוֹב, *fresh,* and פַּשׁ, *overmuch* (*Metzudas David* ad loc.; cf. *Rashi* there and *Mefaresh* here).

19. After he has taken ill and recovered, his physical self will be even stronger and healthier than it was before his illness (*Ran*).

Mefaresh here understands that Rav Hamnuna, like R' Alexandri, is speaking about an illness' atonement for one's sins. Going with this approach, *Iyun Yaakov* and *Iyei HaYam* point out that there is a slight difference between the two statements: R' Alexandri, who says that all the sick person's sins are forgiven, expounds the word הַסֹּלֵחַ, *He Who forgives.* Now, the word סְלִיחָה, *selichah,* connotes an erasure of sin that is less than total (see *Ibn Ezra* to *Numbers* 14:19). His sins are not held against him currently, but they are held in abeyance. If a person continues to sin after he recuperates, his earlier sins will be called into account together with his new ones. However, Rav Hamnuna states that a person recovering from an illness will return to the days of his youth, i.e. he will be restored to his pristine spiritual state in which he had never even tasted sin. If he sins henceforth, it will be as if he is doing so for the first time.

20. *Psalms* 41:4.

21. [In the plain meaning of this verse, Scripture describes how God fortifies a sick person even when his illness is intense and he is restless (see *Rashi* ad loc.).]

22. The neatly arranged blankets and pillows of a made bed are a metaphor for the well-organized knowledge of the Torah in a person's mind. The verse likens the disruption of one's erudition to the chaos of a bed turned upside down (see *Mefaresh;* see *Rif* who finds another common element between a made bed and Torah study).

It seems that *Ran* and *Rosh* had a version of our Gemara that did not cite the verse, *you will have upset all his bedding.* Rather, in their version of our text, Rav Yosef expounds the verse cited above, *he shall return to the days of his youth,* except that he interprets the word עֲלוּמָיו to mean not *his youth* but *his concealments.* The recuperating patient will return to the days of his concealments; i.e. his Torah knowledge will be concealed from him.

Maharal explains that the three phenomena mentioned in our Gemara (the forgiveness of sins, the restoration of youthful health and the loss of one's Torah knowledge)

After citing Rav Yosef's teaching, the Gemara cites an incident that occurred with Rav Yosef himself that bears out this teaching:

רַב יוֹסֵף חֲלַש – **Rav Yosef took ill. As a result,** אִיעֲקַר לֵיה לְמוּדְרֵיה – **his learning was purged** from his memory.[23] אַהְדְרֵיה אַבַּיֵי קַמֵּיה – **Abaye reviewed [everything Rav Yosef had taught him] in front of [Rav Yosef]** and thus restored his learning to him. הַיְינוּ דְּבְכָל דּוּכְתָּא אַמְרִינַן – **That is** the explanation **for every place** in the Talmud **where we say,** אָמַר רַב יוֹסֵף לֹא שְׁמִיעַ לִי הֲדָא שְׁמַעְתָּא – **"Rav Yosef said: I have never heard this teaching,"** and then אָמַר לֵיה אַבַּיֵי אַתְּ – אַמְרִיתָה נֶיהְלַן – **"Abaye told him: You said this [teaching] to us** וּמֵהָא מַתְנִיתָא – **and it was based on this Baraisa that you said it to us."** In the several places where this exchange occurs,[24] Rav Yosef did not recognize a teaching he himself had taught because his illness had erased it from his memory. Abaye then restored the teaching to him by reviewing it and its source before him.

Another incident regarding a sage who became sick and forgot his learning:

כִּי הֲוָה גָּמִיר רַבִּי תְּלָת עֲשְׂרֵי אַפֵּי הִלְכָתָא – **When Rebbi had learned thirteen complete versions of the** early **Mishnah,**[25] אַגְמְרֵיה לְרַבִּי חִיָּיא שִׁבְעָה מִנְהוֹן – **he**

NOTES

are all connected. He states that once a person's physical nature has been damaged, it would be impossible for him to return to complete health except that God enables him to make a new beginning, to become created anew. Since he has made a new start, his old sins are not counted against him, his health is like the health of a youth and the Torah he previously absorbed is no longer with him.

23. *Ran's* version of our text is אִיַּיקַר לֵיה, *his learning became too heavy* [for him to bear and he forgot it]. The basic meaning however is the same.

24. *Mesoras HaShas* lists eight places.

25. Until the era of Rebbi, the *Torah SheBe'al Peh,* the Oral Torah, was transmitted from master to student in any form and in any wording that the master preferred. A master was free to express himself in his own words, as one describes something to one's friend. Nonetheless, a student generally strove to adhere to the form and style that he had received from his master. Each of these traditions was a comprehensive reiteration of the Oral Torah, although some were phrased concisely and others with more elaboration. Torah scholars such as Rebbi were adept in the compilations of different schools. However, in his time this system became too unwieldy for many scholars and Rebbi initiated a new system. He took R' Meir's compilation as a foundation, and together with the Sages of the generation, edited, redacted and perfected the work that would be known as the "Mishnah": From then on, all the scholars studied and memorized this version and all the other compilations became known as Baraisos, "outside material." These were the thirteen versions of the early Mishnah which Rebbi had learned (see *Iggeres Rav Sherira Gaon,* R' N.D. Rabinowich ed., Ch. 3). *Rashi* to *Berachos* 20a states that the thirteen versions included compilations such as the Mishnah itself, R' Chiya's *Tosefta,* and the Baraisos of Bar Kappara, Levi and Shmuel's academy.

[In regard to whether Rebbi actually wrote the Mishnah or simply organized it and determined its final phrasing, see discussion and sources in the *Lev Same'ach* ed. of *Rav Nissim Gaon's Introduction* to *Sefer HaMafte'ach,* note 72, at end of *Rabbeinu Chananel* to *Berachos.*]

taught seven of these complete versions **to R' Chiya.**[26] לְסוֹף חֲלַשׁ רַבִּי – **Ultimately, Rebbi took ill** and forgot his learning. R' – אַהְדַּר רַבִּי חִיָּיא קַמֵּיהּ **Chiya reviewed before him** הְנְהוּ שִׁבְעָה אַפֵּי דְּאַגְמְרֵיהּ – **those seven** complete **versions that [Rebbi] had taught him.** Thus, Rebbi relearned these seven שִׁיתָא אָזְדוּ – but the other **six slipped away.** הֲוָה הַהוּא קַצְרָא – **However, there was a certain laundryman** who הֲוָה שְׁמִיעַ לֵיהּ לְרַבִּי – **had overheard Rebbi** כְּדַהֲוָה גָּרִיס לְהוּ – **whenever [Rebbi] would recite them** out loud.[27] The laundryman thus knew the six missing versions by heart.[28] אֲזַל רַבִּי חִיָּיא וּגְמַר יַתְהוֹן קַמֵּי קַצְרָא – **R' Chiya went and learned them before this laundryman,** i.e. the laundryman taught R' Chiya the six missing versions, וְאָתָא וְאַהְדַּר יַתְהוֹן קַמֵּי רַבִּי – **and [R' Chiya] came back and reviewed them before Rebbi,** restoring them to him.

The Gemara recounts Rebbi's deep gratitude to the person who had helped restore his learning:

כַּד הֲוָה חָזֵי לֵיהּ רַבִּי לְהַהוּא קַצְרָא – **Whenever Rebbi would see that laundryman,** אָמַר לֵיהּ רַבִּי – **Rebbi would tell him,** אַתָּה עֲשִׂיתָ אוֹתִי וְאֶת חִיָּיא – **"You made me and Chiya!** Because of the Torah that you taught us, it is as if you gave us life."[29] אִיכָּא דְּאָמְרֵי הָכִי קָאָמַר לֵיהּ – **There are some who say that this is what [Rebbi] told the [laundryman]:** וְחִיָּיא אַתָּה עֲשִׂיתָ אֶת חִיָּיא – **"You made Chiya** עֲשָׂה אוֹתִי – **and Chiya made me!"**[30]

Another Aggadic teaching regarding a sick person's recovery:[31]

וְאָמַר רַבִּי אֲלֶכְסַנְדְּרִי אָמַר רַבִּי חִיָּיא בַּר אַבָּא – **And R' Alexandri said in the name of R' Chiya bar Abba:** גָּדוֹל נֵס שֶׁנַּעֲשֶׂה לַחוֹלֶה יוֹתֵר מִן הַנֵּס שֶׁנַּעֲשָׂה לַחֲנַנְיָה מִישָׁאֵל וַעֲזַרְיָה – **The miracle that is performed for a sick person** when he returns to health **is greater than the miracle that was performed for Chananyah, Mishael and Azaryah** when they were spared from burning in the

---

NOTES

26. [*Maharsha* offers reasons for why there were *thirteen* compilations and why seven of these were taught to R' Chiya.]

27. The Gemara in *Kesubos* 103b recounts a story about a laundryman who would see Rebbi every day and who died on the same day Rebbi did. This is the same laundryman (*Shitah Mekubetzes*). *Maharal* (to *Kesubos*) writes that this person is called "a laundryman" because he was willing to repent his former ways and wash his soul clean of any spiritual stains.

28. [He may not have known them at any depth, but he did at least know them by rote.]

29. Because whoever teaches his fellow Torah is as if he "made" him, as it says [regarding the persons that Abraham and Sarah taught and brought near to God] (*Genesis* 12:5): *Abram took his wife Sarai and Lot ... and the people they made in Haran* (*Rosh*, citing *Sanhedrin* 99b).

[Although Rebbi and R' Chiya knew seven of the compilations already, the remaining six shed a new light on everything else they knew. Because of this, Rebbi deemed it as if the laundryman had spiritually created him and R' Chiya.]

30. The two versions differ in whether there is a mitzvah for a student to honor his teacher's teacher; see *Maharal* and *Ben Yehoyada*.

31. The following pair of Amoraim was quoted above on this topic.

furnace.[32] The reasoning is as follows: שֶׁל חֲנַנְיָה מִישָׁאֵל וַעֲזַרְיָה אֵשׁ שֶׁל הֶדְיוֹט – The fire **that** endangered **Chananyah, Mishael and Azaryah was an ordinary fire,** וְהַכּל יְכוֹלִים לְכַבּוֹתָהּ – **which,** potentially, **any person could have doused.** וְזוֹ שֶׁל חוֹלֶה שֶׁל שָׁמַיִם הִיא – **However, this** fire, i.e. the fever, that endangers **a sick person** is a fire **from Heaven,** וּמִי יָכוֹל לְכַבּוֹתָהּ – **and who is it that can douse it** other than God?[33]

Another Aggadic statement from the pair of Amoraim quoted twice above:

וְאָמַר רַבִּי אֲלֶכְּסַנְדְּרִי אָמַר רַבִּי חִיָּיא בַּר אַבָּא – **And R' Alexandri said in the name of R' Chiya bar Abba,** וְאָמְרֵי לָהּ אָמַר רַבִּי יְהוֹשֻׁעַ בֶּן לֵוִי – but **some say** it was **R' Yehoshua ben Levi** who **said:** כֵּיוָן שֶׁהִגִּיעַ קִיצוֹ שֶׁל אָדָם – **Once a person has reached the end** decreed **for his** life, הַכּל מוֹשְׁלִים בּוֹ – **any creature can subdue him** in order to bring about his death, שֶׁנֶּאֱמַר – **as it was said** by Cain[34] after God removed His protection from him, „וְהָיָה כָל־מֹצְאִי יַהַרְגֵנִי" – **"Whoever meets me will kill me!"**[35]

NOTES

32. [See *Daniel* Ch. 3.] Nebuchadnezzar, the king of the Babylonian Empire, built a large golden idol and commanded that everyone bow down to it at its inauguration. Whoever would not do so would be cast into a fiery furnace. Several men informed on Chananyah, Mishael and Azaryah, telling the king that they did not bow down to the idol. The king became angry, summoned them and ordered them to bow down at that moment or they would be cast into the fire. They refused and told him that their God would save them from his hand, and that they would not worship his idol in any event, even if they would not merit being saved. Nebuchadnezzar became enraged; he ordered his servants to heat up the furnace until it was seven times as hot as the norm and to throw Chananyah, Mishael and Azaryah in. They tied them up, while still clothed, and threw them in. Afterward, Nebuchadnezzar saw that the fire had no effect on them. He also saw an angel in the furnace with them. Nebuchadnezzar had a change of heart. He summoned them out of the furnace and gave orders that no one should speak disparagingly of the God of Chananyah, Mishael and Azaryah.

33. Certainly [from our perspective], it is more of a wonder that Chananyah, Mishael and Azaryah were not harmed in the center of a raging furnace than that a sick person recovers from his illness. The first defies the natural workings of the world while the second seems to fall well within them. However, the Gemara means that the miracle of healing is greater in another sense: The deliverance of a sick person is carried out through a more sublime spiritual level than was used in the deliverance of Chananyah, Mishael and Azaryah (*Maharal*). *Iyun Yaakov* comments that these three men were perfectly righteous and they deserved, perhaps, to be saved through a miracle. But the average sick person is guilty of some sins and thus God must act despite these sins in saving the sufferer. This requires the forgiveness of sins mentioned by the Gemara above. [Thus, the recovery of a sick person is a more sublime miracle than the deliverance of the three righteous men from the furnace.]

34. *Genesis* 4:14.

35. After Cain murdered Abel, God cursed him to be a vagrant and a wanderer (*Genesis* 4:12). Cain thereby lost the protection of his house and he also lost the Divine protection that every human being enjoys: the assurance that animals will be inhibited from attacking him. Typically, a person is feared by animals, as it says (*Genesis* 9:2): *The fear of you and the dread of you shall be upon every beast of the earth and upon every bird of the heavens, in everything that moves on earth and in all the fish*

The Gemara derives this principle from a different verse:

רַב אָמַר מִן הָדֵין קְרָא – **Rav said** we should expound that idea **from this verse:**[36] „לְמִשְׁפָּטֶיךָ עָמְדוּ הַיּוֹם כִּי הַכֹּל עֲבָדֶיךָ" – *[They are ready to fulfill]* **Your decrees** *[upon]* **those who have stood** *[for judgment]* **today, for all are Your servants.**[37]

An incident that illustrates this principle:

שָׁכִיב גַּבְרָא גָבוֹהַּ – **a tall man had died** in the following way: רַבָּה בַּר שִׁילָא אָמְרוּ לֵיהּ – **Rabbah bar Shila was told** that הֲוָה רָכִיב גִּירְדּוֹנָא זוּטְרָא – **He was riding a small female mule and** מְטָא תִּיתוֹרָא – **he reached a bridge.** While crossing the bridge, אִיסְתְּוִיט שַׁדְיֵיהּ וְקָא שָׁכִיב – **[the mule] went mad,**[38] **threw him off her** and into the river **and he died.** קְרֵי עַל נַפְשֵׁיהּ – **[Rabbah bar Shila] applied the verse** cited above **to him:**[39] „לְמִשְׁפָּטֶיךָ עָמְדוּ הַיּוֹם" – *[They are ready to fulfill]* **Your decrees** *[upon]* **those who have stood** *[for judgment]* **today,** for all are Your servants.[40]

NOTES

of the sea; in your hand they are given. However, when a person sins so grievously that he loses this Divine protection, then instead of ruling over the animals, they rule over him (see *Bereishis Rabbah* 8:12 and *Rashi* to *Genesis* 1:26). This is what happened to Cain. He thus feared for his life at the hand of any creature that might encounter him upon his wanderings. In response to his plea, *God placed a mark upon Cain, that none that meet him might kill him* (*Genesis* 4:15): God restored the fear of him upon the animals (*Rashi* ad loc. in Alkabetz ed. of 1476, reprinted in Sapirstein ed.; see also *Ramban* ad loc.). This awe that man projects upon the animal kingdom is a function of his being created in the image of God; see *Bereishis Rabbah* 8:12 and *Iyun Yaakov* here.

In any case, we find that when God's protection is removed from someone, he is vulnerable to the attacks of any creature. Thus, we may reason, when a person's time comes and Divine protection is taken from him (see *Or HaChaim* to *Genesis* 47:29 who discusses the departure of the Divine image before a person's death), he is liable to be the vanquished prey of any man or beast.

36. *Psalms* 119:91.

37. Rav prefers this verse to the one involving Cain cited above, because the words *Whoever meets me will kill me* imply that a creature is a threat only if it inadvertently encounters him. However, there is no indication from these words that when a person's time has come, God will send a creature from afar as His agent to end the person's life. By contrast, the verse, *[They are ready to fulfill] Your decrees ... for all are Your servants,* indicates that all creatures are God's servants to fulfill His judgments (*Ben Yehoyada;* cf. *Maharsha*).

38. Or, became terrified (*Rosh,* citing *Yoma* 22b). [The translation in the text is based on *Ran,* citing *Bava Kamma* 37b.]

39. The translation follows the many versions of our text that have the words קְרֵי עֲלֵיהּ (see *Dikdukei Soferim HaShalem*). According to the text as we have it (קְרֵי עַל נַפְשֵׁיהּ, *he applied the verse to himself*), it is possible that the Gemara means that Rabbah bar Shila drew a lesson from this incident and took it to heart, or that it was the tall man who applied this verse to himself as he was dying.

40. Even such an unlikely agent of death as a small mule carrying a tall man (whose feet presumably reached the ground) can assume the role of Heaven-sent executioner if that is God's will. In an unguarded moment, the tall man's ability to dismount quickly is to no avail (*Ben Yehoyada;* see *Eitz Yosef*).

A similar incident:

שְׁמוּאֵל חַזְיֵיהּ לְהַהוּא (קרוקיתא ד)עַקְרְבָּא[41] יְתִיבָא עַל אַקְרוֹקְתָא – **Shmuel saw a certain scorpion that was sitting atop a female frog,** וְעָבְרָה נַהֲרָא – **and was crossing the river** using the frog as a ferry. טַרְקָא גַּבְרָא וּמָיֵית – **The scorpion** reached the other side, **stung a man** who was there **and [the man] died.** קְרֵי עֲלֵיהּ – **[Shmuel] applied the** above **verse to him:** „לְמִשְׁפָּטֶיךָ עָמְדוּ הַיּוֹם״ – *[They are ready to fulfill]* **Your decrees** *[upon]* **those who have stood** *[for judgment]* **today, for all are Your servants.**[42]

The Gemara returns to the topic of visiting the sick:

אָמַר שְׁמוּאֵל – **Shmuel said:** אֵין מְבַקְּרִין אֶת הַחוֹלֶה – **One does not visit a sick person** אֶלָּא לְמִי שֶׁחֲלָצַתּוּ חַמָּה – **unless** he has the kind of illness in which **he is wrapped with fever.**[43]

The Gemara inquires:

לְאַפּוּקֵי מַאי – **What** illnesses does Shmuel mean **to exclude** from visits?[44]

The Gemara explains:

לְאַפּוּקֵי הָא דְּתַנְיָא – He means **to exclude that which has been taught in a Baraisa:** רַבִּי יוֹסֵי בֶּן פְּרָטָא אוֹמֵר מִשּׁוּם רַבִּי אֱלִיעֶזֶר – **R' YOSE BEN PERATA SAYS IN THE NAME OF R' ELIEZER:** אֵין מְבַקְּרִין לֹא חוֹלֵי מֵעַיִים – **ONE DOES NOT VISIT THOSE WHO ARE SICK WITH INTESTINAL DISEASES,** וְלֹא חוֹלֵי הָעַיִן וְלֹא מֵחוּשֵׁי הָרֹאשׁ – NOR **THOSE WHO SUFFER FROM EYE DISEASES, NOR** those with **HEADACHES.**

The Gemara analyzes this Baraisa:

בִּשְׁלָמָא חוֹלֵי מֵעַיִים – **It is well** and good why one does not visit **those with intestinal diseases,** מִשּׁוּם כִּיסוּפָא – **because** such visits may result in **embarrassment** for the sick person when he needs to relieve himself.[45] אֶלָּא חוֹלֵי הָעַיִן וּמֵחוּשֵׁי הָרֹאשׁ – **But** in regard to those who suffer from **eye diseases and headaches,** מַאי טַעְמָא – **what is the reason** one should avoid visiting them?

NOTES

41. Emendation follows the text found in all the manuscripts and early printed editions, and *Mesoras HaShas*. The translation follows that version.

42. The scorpion could not swim (*Mefaresh*) and the frog could not sting. They joined forces together to accomplish a mission that neither one could have achieved alone, to bring about the death of a certain man in a certain place at a certain time, *for all are Your servants,* in the plural (see *Maharsha*).

43. [Literally: fever has wrapped him.] I.e. he is feverish (cf. *Rashi* to *Yevamos* 71a ד״ה אלא הכא).

44. It cannot be that Shmuel means that the mitzvah of visiting the sick applies only where the sick person has a fever, and all the other numerous diseases and disorders do not warrant a visit. The sources from which we derive the mitzvah of visiting the sick do not indicate any such qualification and there is no logic for us to impose it on our own. Rather, Shmuel means that the mitzvah applies only to illnesses such as fevers; but certain other illnesses, which for various reasons preclude visits, are excluded from this mitzvah (see *Iyun Yaakov*). What then are the illnesses he means to exclude?

45. [He may be embarrassed to leave the visitor and take care of his needs on every occasion he needs to do so. Also, it is characteristic of those suffering intestinal ailments to emit offensive odors (see *Moed Katan* 27b).]

The Gemara explains:

מְשׁוּם דְּרַב יְהוּדָה – It is **because of** what **Rav Yehudah** said, דְּאָמַר רַב יְהוּדָה – **for Rav Yehudah said:** דִּיבּוּרָא קַשְׁיָא לְעֵינָא – **Speech is harmful for the eye** וּמְעַלֵּי לְאִישְׁתָּא – **and beneficial for a fever.** Since the visitor's presence will prompt a conversation, it is better that he not visit. And since eye diseases and headaches have similar pathologies, speech is harmful for headaches as well.[46]

The Gemara comments on fevers:

אָמַר רָבָא – **Rava said:** One should note the following regarding הַאי אִישְׁתָּא – **this** condition of **fever:** אִי לָאו דִּפַרְוַונְקָא דְּמַלְאָכָא דְּמוֹתָא – **If not** for the fact **that it is an agent of the Angel of Death,** מְעַלֵּי – it would be as **beneficial** for a person

---

NOTES

46. *Rosh* (cf. *Hagahos HaGra*).

[One of the central reasons there is a mitzvah to visit the sick in the first place is the commandment (*Leviticus* 19:18): *You shall love your fellow as yourself* (see above, 39b note 3). That is, just as a person would want others to inquire after him when he is sick and to tend to his needs, so should he strive to do for others. However, in the case of these illnesses a person would not want others to visit him – either because of potential embarrassment or because this would worsen his condition. Therefore, there is no mitzvah to visit such patients. To the contrary, one fulfills the mitzvah *love your fellow as yourself* by *refraining* from such visits.]

However, one should not simply ignore the ailing person. In all the cases, one should inquire of the household members as to the patient's welfare and whether there are any needs to which he may attend. He should also pray for him (*Ramban, Toras HaAdam, Shaar HaMichush* ד״ה תניא ר׳ יוסי; *Yoreh Deah* 335:8).

Halachic Sources

Rambam Hilchos Aveil*
Perek 14

[Ed. note: In this chapter, the Rambam discusses other halachos in addition to those relating to bikur cholim. Our translation will focus exclusively on the halachos of bikur cholim.]

1. *It is a positive commandment d'rabbanan (established by the Rabbis) to visit the sick. [Ed. note: The Rambam lists other mitzvos here as well.] These are included in the mitzvah of gemilus chassadim (acts of kindness) — performed with one's body — that have no prescribed measure. And even though all of these mitzvos were established by the Rabbis, they are included in the general rule of "V'ahavta l'rei'acha kamocha" (love your fellow as you would yourself). All the things that you would want others to do for you, you should do them for your brothers in Torah and mitzvos.*

4. *The commandment of bikur cholim applies to everyone. Even a prestigious person should visit one with a lesser social status. One should visit many times throughout the day, and those who do this mitzvah even more often are praiseworthy, with the caveat that they do not disturb or bother the sick person. One who visits the sick person is considered to have taken away a portion of his illness, making his disease less severe. One who does not visit the sick is likened to one who has shed blood.*

5. *One should visit the sick person only from the third day of his illness and on. However, if the sickness is sudden and quite severe, then one is permitted to visit immediately. One should not visit the sick person in the first or last three hours of the day because that is when the needs of a sick person are being met. One should not visit a person who has intestinal illnesses or eye or head problems (i.e., headaches) because visits under these circumstances are difficult for the choleh.*

6. *One who visits a choleh should not sit on his bed, a chair, a bench, a high platform or place, or above his head. Rather, one should cloak oneself [Ed. note: a sign of solemnity], sit lower than the choleh's head, request mercy from Hashem on his behalf and then leave.*

7. *It appears to me that comforting mourners takes precedence over visiting the sick, because comforting mourners is an act of chesed on behalf of both the living and the deceased.*

---

* English adaptation

רמב"ם הלכות אבל
פרק י"ד

א מצות עשה של דבריהם לבקר חולים ולנחם אבלים ולהוציא המת ולהכניס הכלה וללוות האורחים ולהתעסק בכל צרכי הקבורה לשאת על הכתף ולילך לפניו ולספוד ולחפור ולקבור וכן לשמח הכלה והחתן ולסעדם בכל צרכיהם ואלו הן גמילות חסדים שבגופו שאין להם שיעור אע"פ שכל מצות אלו מדבריהם הרי הן בכלל ואהבת לרעך כמוך כל הדברים שאתה רוצה שיעשו אותם לך אחרים עשה אתה אותן לאחיך בתורה ובמצות:

ב בקור חולים מצוה על הכל אפילו גדול מבקר את הקטן ומבקרין הרבה פעמים ביום וכל המוסיף משובח ובלבד שלא יטריח וכל המבקר את החולה כאילו נטל חלק מחליו והקל מעליו וכל שאינו מבקר כאילו שופך דמים:

ה אין מבקרין את החולה אלא מיום שלישי והלאה ואם קפץ עליו החולי והכביד מבקרין אותו מיד ואין מבקרין את החולה לא בשלש שעות ראשונות ביום ולא בשלש אחרונות מפני שהן מתעסקין בצרכי החולה ואין מבקרין לא חולי מעיים ולא חולי העין ולא מחושי הראש מפני שהבקור קשה להן:

ו הנכנס לבקר את החולה לא ישב לא על גבי מטה ולא על גבי כסא ולא על גבי ספסל ולא על גבי מקום גבוה ולא למעלה ממראשותיו אלא מתעטף ויושב למטה ממראשותיו ומבקש עליו רחמים ויוצא:

ז יראה לי שנחמת אבלים קודם לבקור חולים שנחום אבלים גמילות חסד עם החיים ועם המתים:

Shulchan Aruch Siman 335*
Hilchos Bikur Cholim

1. It is a mitzvah to visit the sick. Close relatives and friends should come and visit immediately (1) and more casual acquaintances should visit after three days. However, if the sickness befell the person suddenly, close friends and relatives as well as more casual acquaintances may visit right away (the Tur, based upon the Ramban).

2. Even an older (i.e., more prestigious) person should visit a sick younger person. And one should do this even many times throughout the day. This is true even for a "ben gilo" (2) (a) (Ed. note: see the Taz and Nedarim 39b for an exact definition). Anyone who does more than this is considered praiseworthy; however, one should not bother the sick person excessively. [Ed. note: One should be very careful not to do so at the sick person's expense.]

The Rema, citing the Maharil, notes that even one who feels hatred toward the sick person is permitted to visit him. But the Rema himself says, "This does not appear to me to be correct." Such a person (i.e., one who feels hatred toward the sick person) should not visit the sick person (b). And likewise, a person should not perform the mitzvah of comforting a mourner for whom he harbors a strong dislike. This is so that the mourner or the sick person should not think that the enemy coming to visit or comfort him is gloating over his illness or misfortune, and the visit will result in only causing pain and suffering. The Rema concludes that this appears to be the correct response.

3. One who comes to visit a sick person should not sit on his bed, nor should he sit on a chair, nor should he sit on a bench. Instead, he should remain fully cloaked and sit in front of the person, recognizing that the Shechinah is most profoundly present at the head of the sick person's bed.

————— **Turei Zahav (Taz)*** —————

(1) The close relatives and friends visit immediately upon hearing that the person is sick: My father-in-law of blessed memory [Ed. note: the Bayis Chadash, the Bach] explains that the reason for this is so as not to jeopardize his mazal by proclaiming that he has the "name" of being sick. To illustrate, the Gemara (Nedarim 40a) states that Rava

————— **Sifsei Kohen (Shach)*** —————

(a) If one is a ben gilo: who removes $\frac{1}{60}$ of the sick person's illness.

(b) Should not visit, etc.: The Bach writes that if one escorts a deceased enemy at his funeral procession, there is no concern that he is gloating on this occasion, as this is the natural end for all human beings (i.e., eventually, everyone will die). However, comforting mourners

*English adaptation

שלחן ערוך סימן של"ה

מתי מבקרין החולה ואיזה חולים מבקרין וכיצד מתפללין עליו.

א מצוה לבקר חולים הקרובים והחברים נכנסים מיד (א) והרחוקים אחר

ג' ימים ואם קפץ עליו החולי אלו ואלו נכנסים מיד. (טור בקינור מס' ח"ה

להרמב"ן):

ב אפי' הגדול ילך לבקר הקטן ואפילו כמה פעמים ביום א ואפילו (ב) בן

גילו וכל המוסיף ה"ז משובח ובלבד שלא יטריח לו: הגה י"א דשונא יכול

לילך לבקר חולה (מהרי"ל ק"ל"ז) ולא נראה לי ב אלא לא יבקר חולה ולא ינחם אבל שהוא שונאו

שלא יחשב ששמח לאידו ואינו לו אלא לצער כן נראה לי (ש"ם פ' כ"ג):

ג המבקר את החולה לא ישב ע"ג מטה ולא ע"ג כסא ולא ע"ג ספסל

אלא מתעטף ויושב לפניו שהשכינה למעלה מראשותיו: הגה ודוקא

טורי זהב

(א) הקרובים והחברים נכנסים מיד. פירש
מו"ח ז"ל הטעם כי היכי דלא ליתרע מזליה
להטיל עליו שם חולה כדאמרינן בנדרים (דף מ')
רבא יומא קמא דחליש אמר לא תגלו לאינשי דלא
ליתרע מזליה כו' אבל קרובים וחברים שנכנסים
תמיד בביתו ליכא הרגשה כ"כ ומ"ה כשקפצן עליו
החולי נכנסים גם הרחוקים מיד:

שפתי כהן

א ואפי' בן גילו – שנוטל ח' מס' בחליו:
ב אלא לא יבקר כו' – וכתב הב"ח דלללווות את
השונא ליכא ליכח למיתש לשמח לאידו באשר הוא סוף
כל האדם אבל לנחם אבל או לבקר חולה שהוא
שונאו יש לחוש לכך ומיהו הכל לפי מה שהוא
השנאה ולפי מה שהם השונאים:

(ב) בן גילו. פי' שנולד בשעתו וניטל ח' מס' מחליו וכן השני ממה ששייר הראשון נוטל חלק ס':

Turei Zahav (Taz)*

would say on the first day of an illness,
"Do not reveal this to other people so
as not to jeopardize my *mazal*." However, informing close relatives and
friends, since they are regularly in the
house, would not elicit this concern [Ed.
note: and they are thus permitted to visit
immediately, since it would not appear
that they are there just to attend to the

Sifsei Kohen (Shach)*

or visiting *cholim* who are one's enemies
does arouse concern and could be misin-
terpreted as gloating. Still, this is totally
dependent upon the circumstances of the
people involved: how great their hatred
was and whether it truly would appear as
if one were gloating if one came to visit
or comfort the parties involved.

sick person, hence their presence would not jeopardize his *mazal*]. This explains
why if the person suddenly became severely ill, even more distant friends and
relatives are permitted to visit immediately. [Ed. note: This concern regarding *mazal*
does not apply in such an instance.]

(2) *Ben gilo:* The definition of a "*ben gilo*" is a person who was born at the same
time as the sick person and has the ability to remove 1/60 of his illness by visiting
him. [Ed. note: This is a metaphysical phenomenon.] Likewise, when a second *ben
gilo* visits, he removes 1/60 of the remaining illness (and so on).

---

*English adaptation

The Rema notes that these rules (just cited by the Mechaber) apply only when the sick person is lying on the floor, because the visitor is thus higher than the sick person. However, if the sick person is lying on a bed, then sitting on a chair or a bench is permissible. [Ed. note: It is disrespectful to be above the sick person since it would appear as if one were sitting higher than Hashem's Presence, Which can be found at the bedside of the sick. However, when the sick person is elevated — lying on a bed, not on the floor — then one is permitted to sit on a chair or a bench because this is not a disrespectful position.] The Rema concludes that this is in fact our custom (quoting this in the name of the Beis Yosef, the Ran, the Hagahos Maimonios, Tosafos and the Hagahos Asheri).

4. People should not visit the sick person during the first three hours of the day because he appears healthiest then; consequently, visitors will not be sufficiently concerned about him and will not pray on his behalf as fervently as they should. Likewise, they should not visit in the last three hours of the day since the sick person then appears to be in more dire straits than he actually is; under those circumstances, visitors will despair of his recovery and fail to pray for him as they should.

The Rema notes that anyone who visits the sick and does not pray for Hashem's mercy on their behalf has not fulfilled the mitzvah appropriately (Beis Yosef in the name of the Ramban).

5. Regarding praying for Hashem's mercy on the sick person's behalf, if one is praying in front of him (c), one can pray in any language with which one feels comfortable. (3) However, if one is praying for the sick person, but not in his presence, one should pray only in the Holy Tongue [Ed. note: Hebrew]. (4)

6. When praying for the sick person [Ed. note: on a weekday], one should beseech Hashem to have mercy upon him, together with all the other cholim of Israel (d). However, on Shabbos, one should

———————————— Turei Zahav (Taz)* ————————————

(3) *One can pray in any language with which one feels comfortable:* We do not say under these circumstances that the heavenly angels, who do not understand Aramaic, will be unable to assist in bringing the prayers before Hashem, because the *Shechinah* is present near the sick person, as the *pasuk* states: "Hashem rests His Presence by the sickbed."

———————————— Sifsei Kohen (Shach)* ————————————

(c) If you beseech in front of the sick person: One can say the prayers in any language because it is as if one is beseeching directly before the Holy Presence Itself, since that Presence is felt especially above the sick person's head. But if one beseeches elsewhere, i.e., not in front of the sick person, the angels do not understand all the languages; see

*English adaptation

כשהחולה שוכב על הארץ דהיושב גבוה ממנו אבל כשהוא שוכב על המטה מותר לישב על כסא וספסל (ב"י בשם הר"ן והגהות מיימוני ותוס' והג"א) וכן נוהגין:

ד אין מבקרין החולה בג' שעות ראשונות של יום מפני שכל חולה מיקל עליו חליו בבקר ולא יחוש לבקש עליו רחמים ולא בג' שעות אחרונות של יום שאז מכביד עליו חליו ויתייאש מלבקש עליו רחמים (וכל שביקר ולא ביקר עליו רחמים לא קיים המצוה) (ב"י בשם הרמב"ן):

ה כשמבקש עליו רחמים ג אם מבקש לפניו יכול לבקש (ג) בכל לשון שירצה ואם מבקש שלא בפניו לא יבקש (ד) אלא בלשון הקדש:

ו יכלול אותו ד בתוך חולי ישראל שיאמר המקום ירחם עליך בתוך חולי ישראל ובשבת אומר שבת היא מלזעוק ה ורפואה קרובה לבא:

טורי זהב

(ג) **בכל לשון שירצה.** ולא שייך כאן אין מלאכי השרת נזקקין ללשון ארמי דשכינה עם החולה שנאמר ה' יסעדנו על ערש דוי וע"כ א"ל אז למלאכים:

(ד) **אלא בלשון הקודש.** משמע דבכל שאר לשונות אין מלאכים נזקקין חוץ מלשון הקודש דוקא והוא דעת הרי"ף הביאו בא"ח סי' ק"א אלא דכ' שם בשם הרא"ש דדוקא ללשון ארמי אין נזקקין אבל שאר לשונות הוי כמו לשון קודש וא"כ קשה על הטור למה סתם כאן נגד אביו ומצריך דוקא לשון הקודש וראה דמשום דחולה בעי רחמי טובא על כן כ' כאן שיעשה אליבא דכ"ע:

שפתי כהן

ג אם מבקש לפניו – הרי מבקש כביכול בפני השכינה עצמה שהרי היא מראשותיו של חולה אבל אם מבקש שלא בפניו אין המלאכי השרת מכירין בכל לשון ועיין בא"ח ס"ס ק"א:

ד בתוך חולי ישראל – שמתוך שכוללו עם אחרים תפלתו נשמעת יותר:

ה ורפואה קרובה לבא – ובא"ח סי' רפ"ז מסיים המחבר ורחמיו מרובים ושבתו שלום וכ"פ הב"ח ע"ש:

Turei Zahav (Taz)*

Therefore, in this case, angels are not needed to bring the *tefillah* to Hashem.

(4) *One should pray only in the Holy Tongue (Hebrew)*: This implies that, in any language other than Hebrew, the angels cannot assist. This is indeed the opinion of the *Rif*, as cited in the *Shulchan Aruch, Orach Chaim, Siman 101*. However, it is written there in the name of the *Rosh* that it is only prayers in Aramaic with which the angels cannot assist because they do not understand it. However, other languages have the same status as Hebrew and when they are used, the angels can assist. Therefore, it is difficult to understand why the *Tur,* here on our *Siman*

Sifsei Kohen (Shach)*

Shulchan Aruch Orach Chaim, end of Siman 101. [Ed. note: Therefore, the prayers in that setting should be recited only in Hebrew.]

(d) *Together with all the other cholim of Israel*: Because he includes all other sick people in his prayers, those prayers are more likely to be answered.

(e) *The recovery is imminent*: In *Orach Chaim, Siman 287,* the *Mechaber* concludes this statement with the words, ''and His mercy is great; and may they (i.e. the *cholim*) rest peacefully,'' as the *Bach* similarly explained; see there (i.e., *Orach Chaim, Siman 287*).

---

*English adaptation

say, "Shabbos is not a day for us to cry out [Ed. note: for mercy], but nevertheless recovery is imminent (e) and certainly will come."

7. One should tell the sick person to attend to his financial concerns. That is, if he has lent or deposited [Ed. note: money or items] with other people, or he has deposits or outstanding loans from other people in his possession, he should make sure that all these matters are addressed. One should not be afraid that death is imminent because one is discussing these matters.

8. One should not visit a person who has diseases of the intestines (f), the eye or the head (g); nor should one visit a person whose illness has come upon him suddenly and makes it difficult for him to speak. One should not visit such a sick person directly [Ed. note: in the room where the sick person is]; instead, one should enter into the outer chamber and inquire about the sick person's needs — asking if there is a need to tidy up, to sweep in front of him or to perform other tasks of this nature. One should listen attentively to the sick person's concerns and suffering and beseech Hashem for mercy.

9. One is permitted to visit non-Jews who are ill in the interest of good will (h).

10. A man should not take care of a woman who has an intestinal illness, (5) but a woman may take care of a man with such a condition (i).

———————— Turei Zahav (Taz)* ————————

[Ed. note: and the Mechaber as well], offers the opinion of the Rif, ignoring the opinion of his own father, the Rosh, and requires specifically that prayers be in He-

———————— Sifsei Kohen (Shach)* ————————

(f) And not for diseases of the intestines: because of the embarrassment that this will cause the sick person.

(g) And not for patients in pain with a

———————————————— Pischei Teshuvah* ————————————————

The Pischei Teshuvah cites the Maharit, who says in the name of the Maharil that one should not recite a "mi shebeirach" (blessing for a sick person) on behalf of one who is not in the immediate vicinity or at a great distance because one is not sure if that person is still living. He is concerned that it might be a wasted or unnecessary blessing, as the sick person may have already succumbed to his illness. However, the Nachalas Shiv'ah argues with this opinion and permits one to make the blessing on the sick person's behalf even in shul on Shabbos, and even if the sick person is in a distant city. He brings a proof to this from the get (divorce) laws, from a case where a man sent a divorce via an agent to his wife, who was living in a distant city. Even though the husband was very elderly or sick, and one might have thought that we should be concerned that perhaps he passed away before the get was delivered, we need not halachically be concerned with this possibility, and we maintain the person's chazakah (status) of being alive. Similarly, we are permitted to recite the "mi shebeirach," under the presumption that the sick person is still living. [Ed. note: In our day, with modern communication, this would generally not be a problem on a weekday, but it could be an issue on Shabbos if the choleh's relatives and friends are not in his vicinity.]

*English adaptation

ז אומרים לו שיתן דעתו על ענייניו אם הלוה או הפקיד אצל אחרים או אחרים הלוו או הפקידו אצלו ואל יפחד מפני זה מהמות:

ח אין מבקרין ו לא לחולי מעים ולא לחולי העין ז ולא לחולי הראש וכן לכל חולי דתקיף ליה עלמא וקשה ליה דיבורא אין מבקרין אותו בפניו אלא נכנסין בבית החיצון ושואלים ודורשין בו אם צריכין לכבד ולרבץ לפניו וכיוצא בו ושומעין צערו ומבקשים עליו רחמים:

ט ח מבקרין חולי עובדי כוכבים מפני דרכי שלום:

י (ה) ט [א] בחולי מעים אין האיש משמש את האשה אבל האשה

(ה) **בחולי מעים כו'.** בד"מ נתן טעם דפרילות כשאים ממשמש לנקיבה בקינוח ודברים כאלו יותר מאשה לאיש כי ילרו של איש גדול מ של אשה ולי נראה הטעם דבחולי מעיים לריך החולה הרבה פעמים להיות לו לסיוע לקום לעשות לרכיו ונמלא שיבא האיש המשמש לאשה חולנית כזאת לידי קישוי כיון דמתעסק בגופה תמיד משא"כ בשאר חולי שא"ל להקימה ולסעדה כ"כ אבל אשה לאיש בכל גווני מותר כי אין כח באיש להתקשות בעת ההיא:

────── שפתי כהן ──────

ו לא לחולי מעיים – משום כיסופא:

ז ולא כו' – שהדבור קשה להם:

ח מבקרין חולי עובדי כוכבים כו' – משמע אפי' חולי עובדי כוכבים לחוד ועי' ל סי' קנ"ח:

ט בחולי מעים כו' – דחיישינן כיון שהיא חולה והוא בריא שמא יבא עליה בע"כ אבל האשה משמשת האיש דכיון שהאיש חולה ליכא למיתב שיבא על אשה בריאה בע"כ דכיון שהיא בריאה והוא חולה יכולה היא שתתגלגל מידו עכ"ל עט"ז והוא מדברי ב"י אבל הד"מ והב"ח והדרישה השיגו על הב"י בזה ופירשו דמדאיתמר דין זה גבי חולי מעים ש"מ דלא שייך אלא גבי חולי מעים דכשנפנית איכא גילוי מלפניו ומאחריה ואיכא חששא דילרו תקפה עליו כו' ע"ש ועט"ל סי' קל"ה ס"ק י"ט ולקמן סי' שנ"ב ס"ג:

[א] **בחולי מעיס** – עט"ז סוף ס"ק ה' ועיין בתשובת גו"ב חלק אה"ע סימן ס"ט:

──────── **Turei Zahav (Taz)*** ────────

brew when recited in the sick person's absence. The *Taz* answers that apparently a sick person is in particular need of great mercy. Therefore, the *Mechaber* wrote here that one should pray in Hebrew, fulfilling all the different opinions (including the more stringent view of the *Rif*).

(5) *Intestinal illness etc:* The *Darchei Moshe* explains that it is an act of impropriety for a man to take care of a woman (e.g., cleaning her or handling similar hygienic needs) after an intestinal

──────── **Sifsei Kohen (Shach)*** ────────

headache: Because talking is difficult for them in such a condition.

(h) One is permitted to visit non-Jews who are ill, etc.: This implies even if there are only non-Jews present; see *Siman* 151 regarding this.

(i) In regard to intestinal illness, etc.: We are concerned that since the woman is sick, and the man is healthy, he may have relations with her against her wishes. However, a woman is permitted to take care of a man because a sick man

---

*English adaptation

The Rema notes that there are those who say that when one has a sick person in his household, he should go to the local sage and ask him to pray for Hashem's mercy on the sick person's behalf. Likewise, the custom is to bless the sick person (j) in the synagogue and to call him by a new name, because a name change results in the decree that has befallen the sick person being ripped up. The Rema concludes that comforting a mourner takes precedence over comforting or visiting the sick (k).

illness. He elaborates that it is more inappropriate for a man to assist a woman than vice versa because his evil inclination and lust are more powerful than those of a woman. The Taz, however, gives his own answer: A person with an intestinal illness will require assistance very frequently, and this constant assistance which involves direct contact with the body of one's wife will more likely lead to potential arousal. This contrasts with other illnesses, where a husband would not be in such close, frequent proximity or contact and would not need to help his wife on such a regular basis. This arousal issue does not apply to a woman caring for a man; her providing care is permissible in all situations. A man's illness and consequently weakened condition mitigate our concern that the man would become aroused by having a woman care for him.

is very unlikely to be able to take advantage of a healthy woman against her will; since she is healthy and he is sick, she would be physically able to resist him. These are the words of the Iturei Zahav, citing the Beis Yosef. However, the Darchei Moshe, the Bach and the Drishah disagree with this Beis Yosef, explaining that since this din is specifically and only cited regarding patients with intestinal illnesses, it must be specific to women with intestinal illnesses who, when they relieve themselves, have to uncover themselves [Ed. note: regularly and to a greater extent], exposing both their front and their back. Under these circumstances, there is a greater concern that a man taking care of a woman with intestinal problems might be overcome by his evil inclination, etc. See there (i.e., those commentaries); and also see Siman 195, Se'if 18, and Siman 352, Se'if 3.

(j) So it is the custom to bless the sick, etc: See Orach Chaim, Siman 54, Se'if 2, where the Rav [Ed. note: the Mechaber, Rabbi Yosef Karo, author of the Shulchan Aruch] writes that there is a custom to bless the sick between the prayer of Yishtabach [Ed. note: the prayer concluding Pesukei D'Zimrah] and the berachah of Yotzer Ohr [Ed. note: the prayer starting the berachos of Krias Shema in Shacharis]. And it is written in Dinim v'Halachos of the Mahariv, Siman 8, that one should not

*English adaptation

משמשת את האיש: הגה י"א שמי שיש לו חולה בביתו ילך אצל חכם שבעיר שיבקש עליו
רחמים (נ"י פ' י"נ) י וכן נהגו [ב] לברך חולים בב"ה לקרא להם שם חדש כי שינוי השם קורע גזר
דינו יא ניחום אבלים קודם לבקור חולים (כל בו):

י וכן נהגו לברך החולים כו' – עיין בא"ח סי' ג"ד ס"ב כתב הרב דיש נוהגין לברך החולה בין ישתבח
ליוצר וכתוב בדינים והלכות של מהרי"ו סי' ח' שאין לברך החולים בשבת ויו"ט וכ"כ בתשובה סי' קט"ו,
ובא"ח ס"ס רפ"ח כ' הרב דמותר לברך בשבת חולה המסוכן בו ביום:

יא ניחום אבלים קודם כו' – שניחום אבלים הוא גמילות חסד שעם החיים ועם המתים וכתב הב"ח
כשא"א לקיים שניהם מניח את החולה ועוסק בנחמות אבלים אבל כשאפשר לקיים שניהם ביקור חולים
קודם כדי לבקש רחמים עליו שיחיה או לרבץ ולכבד לפניו דחשיב כאלו מחייהו ועי"ל ר"מ סי"ב (דין מי
שאסר הנאתו על חבירו אם יכול לבקרו נתבאר בסי' רכ"א סעיף ד'):

[ב] לברך חולים – עיין בה"ט ש של הרב מהרי"ט ז"ל שכתב בשם מהרי"ל שאין לברך החולה כשהוא במקום
אחר. ועיין בשו"ת נחלת שבעה סימן נ"ט שחולק עליו ועשה מעשה לברך חולה בשבת בבהכ"נ אף על
פי שהחולה לא היה שם בעיר רק ביישוב שהיה רחוק מהלך שעה ויותר והביא ראיה מגיעין דאפילו הניחו
זקן או חולה נותן לה בחזקת שהוא קיים וגדול אחד כתב להעמיד דברי מהרי"ל והוא חזר והשיב לו עיי"ש
מסי' ט"ז עד סימן פ"ח:

Sifsei Kohen (Shach)*

recite the blessing for the sick on Shabbos and Yom Tov, and so it is written in
Responsa, *Siman* 115. However, in *Orach Chaim,* end of *Siman* 288, the Rav writes
that it is permissible to recite this blessing on Shabbos for a sick person in great need
on that very day.

(k) Comforting mourners takes precedence, etc.: This is because comforting mourners is considered an act of *chesed* on behalf of both the living and the deceased.
The *Bach* notes that when it is impossible to fulfill both of these two mitzvos — visiting
the sick and comforting mourners — then one should not attend to the sick and deal
with comforting the mourners. However, when it is possible to do both, visiting the
sick takes precedence so that one can beg for Divine mercy on behalf of the ill person
(i.e., praying that he should live) or sweep and clean (i.e., take care of the ill person's
physical needs) if necessary, which is considered comparable to sustaining his life.
Also look further, in *Siman* 240, *Se'if* 12. (The laws pertaining to an individual who
made a personal vow prohibiting himself from providing benefit to a certain person —
would the "vower" be permitted to visit and take care of that person should he
become ill? — are explained in *Siman* 221, *Se'if* 4.)

*English adaptation

חכמת אדם — כלל קנא

דין בקור חולים ורפואה וגוסם. ובו כ"ה סימנים. (מסימן של"ה עד של"ט):

א מצוה לבקר חולים. הקרובים והחברים נכנסים מיד אבל הרחוקים אינם נכנסים אלא אחר ג' ימים כדי דלא ליתרע מזליה להטיל עליו שם חולה ואם קפץ עליו החולי אפילו הרחוקים נכנסים מיד ואפילו הגדול ילך לבקר הקטן ואפילו כמה פעמים ביום ואפילו בן גילו (רצה לומר הנולד בשעתו) שנוטל אחד מששים מחליו אפילו הכי יבקר וכל המוסיף הרי זה משובח. ובלבד שלא יהיה לטורח על החולה אבל השונא לא יבקר חולה ולא ינחם באבלו שלא יחשוב ששמח לאידו ואינו אלא לצער לו אבל ללוותו מותר דזה סוף כל אדם ומיהו הכל לפי השונאים והשנאה

Chochmas Adam — Klal (Chapter) 151
The Laws of Visiting the Sick*

1. It is a mitzvah to visit the sick. Close relatives and friends should visit immediately when they learn that the person is sick. However, friends and relatives who are not as close should not visit for at least three days so as not jeopardize the choleh's mazal by proclaiming that he has the status of being sick. However, if the illness befell him very suddenly, then even friends and relatives who are not close may visit immediately. Even a greater person should go and visit a less prestigious person; this should be done even many times on the same day. Furthermore, even a person who is a "ben gilo" (one who was born at the same time as the sick person and removes ¹⁄₆₀ of his illness) should go and visit many times. Anyone who visits many times is considered praiseworthy; however, this is with the caveat that one not burden the sick person (i.e., cause him/her distress or bother by overly frequent visitations). An enemy should not visit a sick person nor should he go to comfort a mourner, lest the sick person or mourner feel that the enemy is gloating over his misfortune and has come solely to cause him pain and suffering. However, one is permitted to escort the funeral procession of an enemy who passed away, as it is understood that everyone eventually will die. [Ed. note: Since it is the way of the world that both the hater and the one who is hated eventually will pass away, escorting a funeral procession will not be viewed as gloating.] However, every case is different and depends upon the individuals and their level of hatred

---

*English adaptation

(סימן של"ה סעיף א' וב' וש"ך):

ב כשהחולה שוכב על הארץ לא ישב המבקר על גבי ספסל שגבוה ממנו שהשכינה למעלה מראשותיו אבל כשהחולה מוטל במטה מותר (שם סעיף ג'):

ג עיקר מצות ביקור חולים שיבקש עליו רחמים ואם ביקר ולא ביקש לא קיים המצוה ולכן אין מבקרין בג' שעות ראשונות של יום מפני שכל חולה מיקל עליו חליו בבקר ולא יחוש לבקש רחמים ולא בג' שעות אחרונות של יום שאז מכביד עליו חליו ויתיאש מלבקש (שם סעיף ד'):

ד כשמבקש רחמים אם מבקש לפניו יכול לבקש בכל לשון שירצה שהרי מבקש כביכול לפני השכינה שהיא אצל החולה אבל כשמתפלל שלא

Chochmas Adam*

(Yoreh De'ah 335, Se'ifim 1 and 2, and the Shach).

2. When a sick person is lying on the floor, the visitor should not sit on a bench above him, because the Shechinah is above the head of the sick person. [Ed. note: The Shechinah's Presence is especially felt by the head of a sick person, and it thus appears as if the visitor is placing himself above Hashem.] However, if the sick person is lying on a bed, then one is permitted to sit down beside him on a bench (Yoreh De'ah 335, Se'if 3).

3. The most essential component of the mitzvah of visiting the sick is to pray on his behalf for Divine mercy. If one visits the sick and neglects to do this, one has not fulfilled the mitzvah. Therefore, one should not visit a sick person during the first three hours of the day because at that point the person's illness does not appear to be as severe as it actually is, and the visitors will not be inspired to beg for Hashem's mercy on his behalf. Likewise, one should not visit during the last three hours of the day because at that time a person's illness appears more severe. This may cause visitors to give up hope, and despair of beseeching for Divine mercy on his behalf (Yoreh De'ah 335, Se'if 4).

4 When a person is requesting Divine mercy in the sick person's presence, he can make this request of Hashem in any language he desires, because it is as if he is making this request directly in front of the Shechinah, Which is always present at the sick person's bedside. However, when one is praying for a sick person not in his

---

*English adaptation

בפניו דאז מלאכי השרת נזקקין להעלות תפלתו ואינם מכירים בשאר
לשונות ולכן יתפלל דוקא בלשון הקודש (שם סעיף ה') ויכלול אותו בתוך
חולי ישראל שמתוך כך תפלתו נשמעת יותר ויאמר המקום ירחם עליך
בתוך חולי ישראל ובשבת יאמר שבת היא מלזעוק ורפואה קרובה לבא
ורחמיו מרובים ושבתו בשלום (שם סעיף ו'):

ה המבקרים אומרים לו שיתן דעתו על ענייניו אם הלוה או הפקיד אצל
אחרים או אחרים אצלו ואל יפחד מפני זה מהמות (שם סעיף ז'). (וזה
לשון ספר חסידים סימן תשי"ז שמע עצה וקיבל מוסר שמע עצה בחיים
וקיבל עצה מאחרים שהרבה ראיתי שציוו בחליים ובני ביתם לא עשו
מצותם וזהו שנאמר (משלי י"ט, כ') למען תחכם באחריתך. עוד (שם סימן
תשי"ח) כשיקרבו ימי אדם למות יצוה לפני עדים ואפילו לאביו לא יאמין
כל שכן לבניו ולאשתו עד כאן לשונו):

<hr>

Chochmas Adam*

presence, in which case the assistance of the ministering angels to
bring these prayers to the heavens is more necessary, one must pray
specifically in the Holy Tongue (Hebrew) because the angels do not
understand all of the other languages (Yoreh De'ah 335, Se'if 5). In
these prayers, one should include the sick person among all Jews
who are ill because in this merit one's prayers are more likely to be
heard. One should say, "May Hashem have mercy upon you, among
all the sick of Israel." On Shabbos, one should state, "Shabbos is an
inopportune time to entreat Hashem. A recovery is sure to come,
His mercy is abundant and may they (the cholim) rest peacefully"
(Yoreh De'ah 335, Se'if 6).

5. Visitors should advise a sick person to attend to any unresolved
matters, (i.e., settle outstanding financial concerns). If he has
lent or deposited money or items with others — or others have lent
or deposited items with him — he should put his affairs in order.
The choleh should not be afraid that since these matters are being
discussed, it must mean that he is nearing death (Yoreh De'ah 335,
Se'if 7). It is written in Sefer Chassidim, Siman 717: "Listen to
advice and accept mussar. Listen to advice in your lifetime and
accept advice from others, for I have seen many ill people instruct
their family members to do certain things, only to have their wishes
ignored by their household. This is what is referred to in Mishlei
19:20: 'so that you will be wise in the end of your days.'" Furthermore, in Siman 718, the Sefer Chassidim states, "When a person's
days come to an end (i.e., he is about to die), he should command

<hr>

*English adaptation

ו אין מבקרין לא לחולה מעיים משום כיסופא ולא לחולה עין ולחולה ראש שהדבור קשה להם וכן לכל חולה שהדבור קשה לו אין מבקרין אותו בפניו אלא נכנסין בבית החיצון ושואלים ודורשין בו אם צריכין לכבד ולרבץ לפניו וכיוצא בו ושומעין צערו ומבקשים עליו רחמים ומבקרין חולי נכרים מפני דרכי שלום (שם סעיף ח' וט'):

ז בחולי מעיים אין האיש משמש את האשה פן יתגבר יצרו כיון שהוא בריא אבל האשה משמשת את האיש כיון שהוא חולה (שם סעיף י'):

ח נוהגין לברך החולים בבית הכנסת ואם הוא מסוכן מותר לברך אפילו בשבת ויום טוב וילך אצל חכם שבעיר שיבקש רחמים עליו (הג"ה סעיף י' וש"ך ס"ק י'):

Chochmas Adam*

his family in front of witnesses [Ed. note: to ensure that his wishes are carried out precisely]; even his father should not be trusted, and certainly not his sons or his wife." Until here is his language (i.e., that of the Sefer Chassidim).

6. *One should not visit a sick person who has intestinal problems because it will embarrass him (i.e., the choleh); nor should one visit a sick person with eye problems or headaches, because speaking is difficult for him. Likewise, one should not visit face-to-face with any choleh for whom speaking is difficult. In these circumstances, one should enter his outer house [Ed. note: antechambers or rooms where the family members are present] and inquire after him — regarding whether cleaning or sweeping is required or whether similar tasks need to be performed. One should hear about the sick person's suffering and beseech Divine mercy on his behalf. One is permitted to visit ill non-Jews in the interest of good will (Yoreh De'ah 335, Se'ifim 8 and 9).*

7. *A man should not take care of a woman who has intestinal problems because perhaps his evil inclination will overcome him while he is caring for her, since he is healthy. However, a woman is permitted to take care of a man in such a situation because he is sick [Ed. note: i.e., he is unlikely to be aroused and/or he is too weak to commit any acts of impropriety] (Yoreh De'ah 335, Se'if 10).*

8. *The custom is to bless a sick person (i.e., to beseech Hashem to heal the choleh) in shul; and if he is very sick, it is permissible to do so even on Shabbos and Yom Tov. Likewise, one should go and visit the sage of the city so that he will beseech Hashem to have*

---

*English adaptation

ט ניחום אבילים קודם לביקור חולים דניחום אבילים הוא גמילות חסדים
לחיים ולמתים וזה דוקא כשאי אפשר לקיים שניהם אבל כשאפשר לקיים
שניהם ביקור חולים קודם כדי שיבקש רחמים עליו שיחיה או לכבד ולרבץ
לפניו דהוי כאילו מחייהו (שם וש"ך ס"ק י"א):

י חולה שמת לו מת אין מודיעין לו שמא תטרף דעתו עליו ואפילו אם
נודע לו אין מצוים לו לקרוע שמא תגדל דאגתו ואין בוכין ואין מספידין
בפניו בין על מתו ובין על מת אחר אף על פי שאינו קרובו שיפחד שגם הוא
ימות ומשתקין את המנחמין אפילו אינו קרובו שעל ידי זה נזכר למיתת
אותו פלוני (סימן של"ז):

יא המנהג בקהלות קדושות ובפרט בק"ק ברלין כשאדם חולה ביום ג'
לחליו (כדאמר רבא הכריזו דחלש) הולכין אליו גבאי ביקור חולים

--- Chochmas Adam* ---

mercy on the sick person (Yoreh De'ah 335, Rema Se'if 10, and Shach note 10).

9. *The obligation to comfort mourners takes precedence over visiting the sick, because comforting mourners is an act of chesed for both the living and the deceased. However, this is so only when it is not possible to fulfill both mitzvos. When it is possible to do both, visiting a sick person comes first so that you can pray for Hashem's mercy on his behalf so that he should live, or so that you can sweep and clean for him (i.e., take care of his physical needs) because this is comparable to saving his life (Yoreh De'ah 335, Rema Se'if 10, and Shach note 11).*

10. *If a sick person's relative passes away, we do not tell him this news because it might upset him [Ed. note: and worsen his condition]. Even if he finds out, we should not make him tear his garments in mourning because this might increase his anxiety. Likewise, we should not mourn nor eulogize a deceased person (whether or not he was the choleh's relative) in his presence because this may cause him to fear that he too will die. Similarly, we silence those who come to comfort the choleh regarding the deceased person (whether or not the deceased was his relative), because we are concerned that this will remind him that he might die, i.e., it may worsen the sick person's condition (Yoreh De'ah 337).*

11. *The custom among many holy congregations, especially in the holy congregation of Berlin, was that when an individual was sick, the person in charge of the bikur cholim society (or some*

---

*English adaptation

או שאר אנשים ואומרים לו אתה ידעת שכן הוא התקון והמנהג אצל כל
החולים ולכן אין לך לדאוג מזה כלום ולכן תעשה צואה מה שתרצה ומה
שאתה חייב או אחרים חייבין לך ועוד אומרים לו התודה כי כל המתודה
על חטאיו מוחלין לו וכיון שבאותן הקהילות המנהג כן אין החולה דואג
מזה כלום וכן ראוי לתקן בכל עיר ועיר אך במקום שאין מנהג זה אין
אומרים כן לחולה שמא ידאג על מיתתו שכן דרך ההמון לדאוג
כשאומרים לו התודה ומכל מקום כשרואין המבקרים שנטה למות
מסבבים עמו בדברים ואומרים לו התודה ואל תדאג מזה כי הרבה התודו
ולא מתו והרבה שלא התודו ומתו ובשכר שאתה מתודה אתה חי וכל
המתודה יש לו חלק לעולם הבא ואם אינו יכול להתודות בפיו יתודה
בלבו ואם אינו יודע להתודות אומרים לו אמור יהי רצון שתהא מיתתי

Chochmas Adam*
---

other person) would visit him on the third day of his illness (as per Rava's instructions in Nedarim 39b) and tell him, "It is our custom to visit all sick people at this time, so do not let our visit cause you any concern. We advise you to prepare a directive (i.e., a last will and testament), delineating your wishes, including any outstanding obligations you have toward others or vice versa [Ed. note: in short, put your financial and other affairs in order]." They would also tell him to recite Viddui (confession) because all who confess their sins to Hashem will be pardoned. Since the representatives of these congregations say this to everybody who is ill, the sick person will not become overly concerned that they have singled him out. Therefore, it is appropriate to institute this practice in every single city. However, where such a custom is not in place, one should not say this to the sick person because he may become overly anxious about his seemingly imminent demise [Ed. note: i.e., he will worry that this advice was directed specifically at him and is an indication that his condition is critical]. After all, it is natural for a person to become very worried when someone tells him to recite Viddui. However, where it is obvious to the visitors that the sick person is nearing death, they should gather around and tell him to recite Viddui, clarifying that he should not be anxious because many people have recited Viddui and did not die, while many others unfortunately did not have the opportunity to recite Viddui and did pass away. They should add, "Hopefully, the merit of reciting Viddui will allow you to live." Furthermore, anyone who recites Viddui has a share in the World to Come. If the choleh cannot recite Viddui aloud, he should

---

*English adaptation

כפרה על כל עונותי. ואין אומרים כל אלו הדברים בפני עמי הארץ ולא
בפני נשים וקטנים שמא יבכו וישברו לב החולה אלא מוציאין אותן לחוץ
וגם יאמרו לו שיבקש מחילה לכל מי שחטא כנגדו בין בממון ובין
בדברים (סימן של"ח סעיף א'):

יב סדר וידוי שכיב מרע לרמב"ן. יעשה צואה ויבקש מחילה לכל מי
שחטא ויבקש וירבה מרבים שיעזרוהו בתפלה ויעשה תשובה שלימה דהיינו
שיגמור בלבו שלא לשוב עוד לעשות מכל מה שעשה ויטול ידיו (ויברך על
נטילת ידים כן כתב רבינו ירוחם נתיב כ"ח חלק א' וצריך עיון) ויתעטף
בציצית ויאמר ה' אלהים אמת ותורתו אמת ומשה נביאו אמת וברוך שם
כבוד מלכותו לעולם ועד ויקרא אשרי יושבי וגו' עד סוף המזמור ומזמור
תפלה לדוד הטה ה' אזניך מזמור פ"ו. ומזמור ד' למנצח מזמור לדוד
בקראי ענני. ומזמור קכ"א אשא עיני וגו'. ואחר כך וידוי שכיב מרע וזה
נוסחתו מודה אני לפניך ה' אלהינו ואלהי אבותינו אלהי אברהם יצחק
ויעקב אלהי האלהים ואדני האדונים בשמים ממעל ועל הארץ מתחת אין
עוד, עושה שמים וארץ עושה חסד ומשפט בארץ, היה הוה ויהיה
שרפואתי בידך ומיתתי בידך, יהי רצון מלפניך שתרפאני רפואה שלימה כי
אתה אל רופא רחמן, ואם אמות תהא מיתתי כפרה על כל חטאי ועוונותי
ופשעי שחטאתי ושעויתי ושפשעתי לפניך, ותן חלקי בתורתך ובגן עדן
וזכני לעולם הבא הצפון לצדיקים. ואני מודה ומאמין שהאל הבורא יתברך

*say it in his heart. If he does not know how to recite Viddui, we tell
him to say, "May it be Your will, Hashem, that my death be a
kapparah (atonement) for all of my sins." One should not say these
things in the presence of unlearned people, women or children
because they may cry, breaking the choleh's heart (i.e., worsening
his condition). Rather, one should have those people leave (before
telling the sick person to recite Viddui). Furthermore, one should
tell the sick person to request mechilah (forgiveness) from anyone he
may have wronged, be it financially or verbally (Yoreh De'ah 338,
Se'if 1).*

12. This paragraph provides the Viddui text, as written by the
Ramban, for a deathly ill person to recite. It also clarifies the
need for the choleh to give a final directive and ask mechilah from
all whom he has wronged. [Ed. note: If this text is unavailable or
cannot be recited, the person should just say, "Let my death be an
atonement for all the sins I have committed."]

*English adaptation

שמו הוא ברא כל העולמות והאציל ובּרא ויצר ועשה, והוא המשגיח לבדו
בכל העולמות ואין שום מציאות לכל העולמות בלתי השגחתו, ומאהבתו
את אבותינו בחר בעמו ישראל ונתן לנו תורתו אשר היא נצחית וקיימת על
ידי נאמן ביתו משה רבינו ועל ידו נתן תורה שבכתב שהיא תורתנו
הקדושה אשר בידינו וגם מסר לו בעל פה פירוש התורה והיא הגמרא
הקדושה אני מאמין שזה מסר הקב"ה למשה ומאמין שדבר עם נביאיו
הקדושים והם ספרי נביאים וכתובים ואני מאמין שיבא לעמו ישראל
משיח צדקינו כאשר נהיה ראוים לפניו לגאלנו ושיחיו המתים, וכשהשעה
דחוקה יזקוף אצבעותיו למעלה ויאמר רבונו של עולם הריני מקבל עלי
מיתה בפועל ממש בשמחה ובלב שלם לקיים מצות עשה כוללת כל
המצות ותיקון כל הלאוין שכולן נתקן לעשה להעביר מחשבת יצר הרע
אשר חפץ להדיח נשמתי מעבודת הקודש והנני מוסר גופי ונפשי ורוחי
ונשמתי על יחוד שמו הגדול (עיין יונת אלם (להרמ"ע מפאנו) פרק ט')
וזכני ליחד שם קדשך באהבה רבה וחיבה יתירה לסלקא יקרא מתתא
לעילא לאתר דשקיא עמיקא דבירא נגיד ונפיק ותהי המסירת נפשי בסוד מי
נוקבא ליחדא קודשא בריך הוא ושכינתיה ברחימו ודחילא ביחודא שלים
ולבתר לאמשכא מעילא לתתא מההוא שקיא דנחלא לכל דרגא ודרגא עד
דרגא בתראה ולקשרא קשרא דכולא כמו שנאמר כי שם ה' אקרא הבו וגו'
יהי רצון מלפניך שיהא שלום מנוחתי ויכוין בשם יתעלה ובמעמד הר סיני
ויאמר שמע ישראל וגו' ברוך שם כבוד מלכותו לעולם ועד. ולפי צחות
החולה כן יאריך בדברי וידוי ותחנונים. ויאמר עלינו לשבח עד על כן נקוה
לך ואמת ויציב עד עזרת (רבינו ירוחם ועוד):

יג הגוסס הרי הוא כחי לכל דבריו ליתן גט ולמתנה, ולענין כהן אם מותר
ליכנס בבית שיש בו גוסס יש מתירין ויש אוסרין ומכל מקום אין
צריכים להקיצו ולהגיד לו כשיש גוסס כמו שצריכין להקיצו כשיש מת
כדלקמן כלל קנ"ט סימן י"ז וכן אם הגידו לו והוא ערום מותר להמתין עד
שילבש עצמו ואחר כך יצא ויקרוב הדבר לומר שאין צריך לצאת כלל מבית
שיש בו גוסס דדוקא לכתחלה אסור ליכנס אלא שנכון להחמיר ולצאת
(סימן ש"ע ש"ך ס"ק ד' וסימן של"ט):

13-15: *[Ed. note: These paragraphs outline the halachos regarding a goseis (a person extremely close to death); we will not translate these halachos here.]*

*English adaptation

יד אסור לעשות דבר לקרב מיתתו ולכן אין קושרין לחייו כדי שלא יפתח
פיו ואין שומטין הכר מתחתיו ואין נותנין אותו על גבי חול כדי
שלאחר שימות לא יחממו אותו הכרים כללו של דבר שלא יגע בו כלל וכל
הנוגע בו הרי זה שופך דמים ולמה הדבר דומה לנר מטפטף שכיון שנוגע
בו אדם מיד נכבה ואין קורעין ואין חולצין ולא מספידין עליו ולא מכניסין
עמו ארון לבית עד שימות ואין פותחין עליו בצדוק הדין עד שתצא נפשו
וכן אין חוצבין לו קבר עד אחר שימות ומכל מקום כיון דמצד הדין מותר
אם אין החולה מרגיש בזה ולכן אם הוא בערב שבת וחוששין שמא לא
יספיקו לקוברו וגם אסור להניחו פתוח ולכן צריך לשער שיהיה שהות
שאם לא יספיק לקוברו אזי יסתמו הקבר ברויח קודם שבת (ש"ך ס"ק ו')
ואסור לחצוב שום קבר להיות פתוח עד למחר שלא יקברו בו המת באותו
היום ויש סכנה בדבר וכן אסור לגרום שימות מהרה אף על פי שהוא גוסס
זמן ארוך ויש צער גדול למת ולקרוביו ואסור להשמיט הכר והכסת
מתחתיו מכח שאומרים שיש נוצות מקצת עופות שגורמים זה וכן לא יזיזנו
ממקומו או לשום מפתחות בית הכנסת תחת ראשו כל זה אסור אבל אם יש
שם דבר שגורם עיכוב יציאת הנפש כגון שיש שם באותו בית קול דופק
כגון חוטב עצים וכיוצא בו מותר להסירו דאין בזה מעשה כלל אלא
שמסיר המונע ואינו נוגע בו כלל (שם סעיף א' ורמ"א):

טו מי שאמרו לו ראינו קרובך גוסס היום שלשה ימים צריך להתאבל
עליו דודאי כבר מת דדוקא בעודו לפנינו חשוב כחי אבל לא כשאינו
לפנינו (שם סעיף ב'):

טז כיון שנטה אדם למות אין רשאי ליפרד ממנו כדי שלא תצא נפשו
והוא יחידי מפני שהנפש משתוממת בשעה שיוצאת מן הגוף ומצוה
לעמוד על האדם בשעת יציאת נשמה שנאמר (תהלים מ"ט, י' — י"א) ויחי
עוד לנצח לא יראה השחת כי יראה חכמים ימותו וגו' (סימן של"ט סעיף

Chochmas Adam*
---

16. When a person's death is imminent, it is improper for those
present to leave him unattended because his soul should not
depart while he is alone. The soul is in distress at the moment it takes
leave of the body (i.e., leaving the body is a very difficult process), and
it is a mitzvah to stay with the person when his soul departs, as it is
stated (Tehillim 49:10-11), "Can one live forever and not see the pit?
Though he sees wise men dying," etc. (Yoreh De'ah 339, Se'if 4). A
person performing this mitzvah should discuss words of Torah with

---
*English adaptation

ד') וידברו עמו דברי תורה או יאמר תהלים (ספר חסידים):

יז מנהג לשפוך כל המים שאובים שבשכונת המת דהיינו ג' בתים והטעם שידעו הכל שיש בו מקרה מות ולא יצטרך להודיע בפה ויהא מוציא דבה ועוד שמלאך המות מפיל במים טפת דם המות (שם סעיף ה'):

יח לאחר שמת לא יזיזו אותו תיכף שמא נתעלף אלא ישהה מעט ונוהגין להניח אצל נחיריו נוצה ואם נשאר מונח שם בידוע שמת ואז אומרים תיכף צדוק הדין וכשמגיע לדיין האמת קורע האבל (שם סעיף ג') והעומדים שם כמבואר בכלל שאחר זה סימן ד' ועכשיו נוהגין לומר צדוק הדין בבית הקברות ויש שאומרים אותו בעוד שהמת עדיין בבית ונראה לי דהאבלים יאמרו תיכף כמו שכתוב בשלחן ערוך כי כן עיקר הדין ואם הוא יורש את המת מברך גם כן שהחיינו כמבואר בחיי אדם כלל ס"ב סימן י"א ומברכין ברכת דיין אמת אפילו בשבת ויום טוב (רוקח סימן של"ז):

— **Chochmas Adam*** —

the dying person [Ed. note: if possible, and appropriate, for the patient in his condition] or recite Tehillim (Sefer Chassidim).

17. The custom [Ed. note: no longer prevalent] was to spill out all of the drawn water in the "neighborhood" (vicinity); i.e., three houses around the deceased. The purpose of this custom was to let people know that someone had passed away without having to personally make such an announcement, as it is preferable not to be the bearer of bad tidings. Furthermore, the Angel of Death places in these waters a drop of the "blood of death" [Ed. note: therefore, they are not suitable for drinking or other usage] (Yoreh De'ah 339, Se'if 5).

18. After the person has expired, one should not immediately remove the body, because perhaps he has only lost consciousness [Ed. note: if one moves him in this state, one might actually cause his death]. Therefore, one should wait a bit. The custom was to verify death by placing a feather near his nostrils, and if it lay there without any sign of movement, one could be certain that the person had truly passed away. [Ed. note: A completely motionless feather indicates a lack of respiration.] Those present should immediately say the Tzidduk Hadin prayer, acknowledging that Hashem's judgment is righteous.

[Ed. Note: The Chochmas Adam discusses additional customs regarding the proper time to say this prayer as well as other non-bikur cholim issues throughout the rest of this paragraph and chapter; these are not included here.]

---

*English adaptation

ערוך השלחן יורה דעה
סימן שלה
הלכות ביקור חולים

א גרסינן בשבת [ל"ב א] לעולם יבקש אדם רחמים שלא יחלה שאם
יחלה אומרים לו הבא זכות והפטר וכו' אדם יוצא לשוק יהא דומה
בעיניו כאלו נמסר לסרדיוט חש בראשו יהי דומה בעיניו כאלו נתנוהו
בקולר עלה למטה ונפל יהי דומה בעיניו כמו שהעלוהו לגרדום לידון
שכל העולה לגרדום לידון אם יש לו פרקליטין גדולים נצול ואם לאו
אינו נצול ואלו הן פרקליטין של אדם תשובה ומעשים טובים ע"ש ולכן
יתן כל אדם אל לבו ובפרט בעת חליו ולא יסמוך על הרופאים לבד
כדכתיב באסא [דברי הימים ב', טז, יב] וגם בחליו לא דרש את ד' רק
ברופאים ויקבל עליו להטיב דרכיו ויחלק צדקה לפי ערכו כדכתיב
וצדקה תציל ממות ויבטח בד' כי יקימנו מחליו ורוב חולים לחיים ואפלו

— Aruch HaShulchan* —

Aruch HaShulchan — Siman 335
Hilchos Bikur Cholim*

1. *The Gemara in Shabbos (32a) states that a person should always beg for Hashem's mercy to spare him from illness, because if he becomes ill, they [Ed. note: the Heavenly Court] will tell him, "List your merits to show that you are worthy of being cured." Elaborating further, the Gemara states that when a person goes to the marketplace, he should envision himself being placed in the custody of an officer of the law; if he has a headache, he should envision himself being bound in chains; if he becomes bedridden, he should envision himself on trial, aware that one who is on trial is judged. If he has excellent defense attorneys [Ed. note: if he has merit], he will be saved; if not, he will not be saved. The person's defense attorneys are his acts of repentance and his good deeds. [Ed. note: This concludes the Aruch HaShulchan's citation of the Gemara in Shabbos.] Therefore, every person should resolve, especially when he is sick, not to rely exclusively on doctors, unlike Asa [Ed. note: one of the great kings of Israel] who, during his illness, turned to doctors instead of to Hashem. One should resolve to improve his ways, to give tzeddakah according to his means (as it is written (Mishlei 10:2), "And charity will save one from death"), to trust that Hashem will*

---

*English adaptation

תשע מאות ותשעים ותשעה מלמדים עליו חובה ואחד מלמד עליו זכות
ניצול שנאמר אם יש עליו מלאך מליץ אחד מני אלף להגיד לאדם ישרו
ויחננו ויאמר פדעהו מרדת שחת מצאתי כופר [איוב לג, כד ופדעהו כמו
פדאהו דאותיות אחהע״ר מתחלפים]:

ב ביקור חולים הוא מהמצות היותר גדולות והוא מדברים שאוכל
פירותיהן בעוה״ז והקרן קיימת לו לעוה״ב כדתנן במשנה דאלו דברים
וכו׳ והיא בכלל גמילות חסדים [ב״מ ל׳ ב] וזהו שאמרה תורה והודעת
להם את הדרך אשר ילכו בם [שם] ומאי דכתיב אחרי ד׳ אלקיכם תלכו וכי
אפשר לו לאדם להלך אחר השכינה והלא כבר נאמר כי ד׳ אלקיך אש
אוכלה הוא אלא להלך אחר מדותיו של הקב״ה מה הוא מלביש ערומים
דכתיב ויעש ד׳ אלקים לאדם ולאשתו כתנות עור וילבישם אף אתה הלבש
ערומים מה הקב״ה ביקר חולים דכתיב וירא אליו ד׳ באלני ממרא אף אתה

─────────── Aruch HaShulchan* ───────────

support him during his illness and to have confidence that most sick
people recover. And even if 999 are arguing against you [Ed. note:
in the Heavenly Court] and [only] one is arguing in your favor and
finding merit, you can be saved (as it is written, Iyov 33:23-24), "If
someone has even one angel out of a thousand advocating for him
and declaring his righteousness, then He will have mercy upon him
and say, 'Redeem him from falling into destruction; I have found
atonement'").

2. Visiting the sick is among the greatest mitzvos. It is one of those
precepts whose fruits a person eats in this world and whose
principal remains for him in the World to Come, as is stated in the
Mishnah [Ed. note: Pe'ah 1:1, and also expanded upon in Shabbos
127a], "These are the precepts," etc. This mitzvah is included in the
category of gemilus chassadim (as stated in Bava Metzia 30b), about
which the Torah says, "You shall make known to them the path
upon which they shall go" and "You shall follow Hashem, your
God." Is it possible for man to walk in the path of the Shechinah? Is
it not written that Hashem, your God, is like a consuming fire [Ed.
note: and, consequently, walking in His path is not possible]? Therefore, the Torah is telling us to emulate the characteristics and traits
of Hashem. Just as Hashem clothes the naked (as it is written,
"Hashem Elokim made for Adam and his wife garments of skin,
and he clothed them"), so too shall you clothe the naked. Just as
Hashem visits the sick (as it is written, "Hashem appeared to Avra-

─────────
*English adaptation

תבקר חולים הקב"ה ניחם אבלים כדכתיב ויהי אחרי מות אברהם ויברך
אלקים את יצחק בנו אף אתה נחם אבלים הקב"ה קובר מתים דכתיב
ויקבור אותו בגיא וגו' אף אתה קובר מתים [סוטה י"ד א] וזהו נכלל בקרא
דאחרי ד' אלקיכם תלכו:

ג עיקר מצות ביקור חולים הוא לעיין בצרכי החולה ולעשות לו מה
שצריך כדאיתא בנדרים [מ' א] מעשה בתלמיד אחד מתלמידי ר"ע
שחלה וכו' ונכנס ר"ע לבקרו ובשביל שכיבד וריבץ לפניו חיה א"ל רבי
החייתני יצא ר"ע ודרש כל שאינו מבקר את החולים כאלו שופך דמים ומה
יפו החברות בכמה ערים הנקראים חברה לינה שלנים אצל החולים כל
הלילה לראות מה שהם צריכים דביום ע"פ רוב משמשים לו אנשי ביתו
משא"כ בלילה דאנשי ביתו עמלים מעבודת היום ונשקעים בשינה באונס

Aruch HaShulchan*
---

ham in Eilonei Mamrei" [Ed. note: Hashem visited Avraham Avinu
following his circumcision because Avraham suffered great pain]), so
too shall you visit the sick. Just as Hashem comforts mourners (as it
is written, "And it was after the death of Avraham that Hashem
blessed his son Yitzchak"), so too shall you comfort mourners. Just
as Hashem buries the dead (as it is written, "And He buried him [Ed.
note: Moshe] in Gai . . ."), so too shall you bury the dead (Sotah
14a). And this is all included in the pasuk, "In the ways of Hashem,
your God, shall you walk."

3. The essential part of the mitzvah of bikur cholim is to investigate the needs of the choleh and to do whatever he requires, as
is stated in the Gemara (Nedarim 40a): There once was an incident
regarding a certain student of Rabbi Akiva who became ill, etc.
Rabbi Akiva went to visit him, and because Rabbi Akiva cleaned up
and sprinkled the floor [Ed. note: floors were made of dirt, and were
kept less dusty by frequent dampening with water or wine] in front
of him, the student survived. The student said, "Rebbi, you have
saved my life." Rabbi Akiva went out and expounded, "Anyone who
does not visit the sick can be compared to one who has shed blood."
And how beautiful it is that in many cities, groups of people —
called chevros linah — stay with cholim all night long and look after
their needs. During the day, in general, most of the cholim's needs
are met by their relatives, but at night, as much as they wish to stay
awake, the relatives are exhausted from working all day and caring
for the choleh. Therefore, very, very great is the reward for these

---

*English adaptation

על כן גדול שכרם מאד מאד של חברי של לינה ואמרו חז"ל [שם] כל המבקר
את החולה נצול מדינה של גהינם ומה שכרו בעוה"ז ד' ישמרהו מיצה"ר
ויחייהו מן היסורין ויאושר בארץ שיהו הכל מתכבדים בו וכו' ע"ש וכל
המבקר את החולה גורם לו שיחיה שמתפלל עליו שיחיה וכל שאינו מבקר
אין מבקש עליו רחמים לא שיחיה ולא שימות דלפעמים יש לבקש רחמים
שימות כגון שיש לו יסורים הרבה בחליו ואי אפשר לו שיחיה כמעשה
דרבי פ' הנושא [ר"ן שם]:

ד יש ליזהר בביקור חולים שלא יהיה המבקר למשא על החולה דלפעמים
יש שקשה עליו הדיבור ומפני כבוד המבקר מוכרח לדבר וגם יש
שצריך לצרכיו והוא בוש לומר לו ולכן צריך להיות זהיר וחכם ומבין בזה
ומטעם זה אמרו חז"ל [שם מ"א א] אין מבקרין לא לחולי מעיים ולא
לחולי העין ולא לחולי הראש דהדיבור קשה להן וחולי מעיים משום שמא
יבוש לומר שצריך לצרכיו וכיצד יעשו נכנסים בבית החיצון לא בהחדר

——— Aruch HaShulchan* ———

chevros linah. As the Sages said, "Anyone who visits the sick will be
saved from Gehinnom. What is his reward in this world? Hashem
will protect him from his evil inclination and relieve his suffering,
and all people will honor him," etc. (see there for more details).
Furthermore, anyone who visits the sick enables them to live because he prays for them. And anyone who does not visit a choleh is
not beseeching Hashem's mercy on his behalf to let him live or to let
him die — because sometimes one needs to pray that he should die,
for example, if he suffers excessively from his illness and recovery is
impossible, as was the case with Rebbi in Perek HaNosei (see the
Ran there) (Ed. note: Kesubos 104a).

4. When visiting a choleh one must avoid burdening him, because
at times, even though it might be difficult for him to speak, he
will feel obligated to converse out of respect for the visitor. Also,
sometimes one will have to help him take care of his bodily functions and this might embarrass him. Therefore, one must be very
careful, wise and understanding in this regard. For this reason our
Sages said (Nedarim 41a) that one should not visit a choleh who has
intestinal problems, nor one who has problems with his eyes, nor
one who has problems with his head, because speaking is difficult
for him. And one with intestinal problems (should not be visited)
because he may be embarrassed to state that he has to take care of
his personal needs. Therefore, what should one do for a person in

*English adaptation

שהחולה שוכב שם ושואלים ודורשים מבני הבית אולי צריך דבר מה ושומעין צערו ומבקשים רחמים ומתפללים עליו:

ה הקרובים והחברים נכנסים מיד שיחלה והרחוקים אחר ג׳ ימים כי היכי דלא יתרע מזליה להקרא עליו שם חולה אמנם אם קפץ עליו החולי בחזקה אלו ואלו נכנסים מיד ואפילו הגדול ילך אצל הקטן ואפילו כמה פעמים ביום ואפילו הוא בן גילו שנוטל אחד מששים מחליו [ב״מ ל׳ א] וכל המוסיף ה״ז משובח ובלבד שלא יהא למשא על החולה כמ״ש בסעי׳ הקודם:

ו כתב רבינו הרמ״א בסעי׳ ב׳ י״א דשונא יכול לילך לבקר חולה ולא נ״ל אלא לא יבקר חולה ולא ינחם אבל מי שהוא שונאו שלא יחשוב ששמח לאידו ואינו לו אלא צער עכ״ל ומיהו הכל לפי מה שהיא השנאה ולפי מה

Aruch HaShulchan*
---

this condition? He should enter the house's outer chamber (not the room where the sick person is actually lying), inquire of the household members what the choleh's needs are, listen to descriptions of his anguish and beseech Hashem's mercy on his behalf.

5. Close relatives and friends should visit the choleh as soon as he becomes sick. More distant acquaintances should visit after three days to avoid jeopardizing his mazal by declaring him a sick person. [Ed. note: "Mazal" is loosely translated as fortune or status, but it is really much more than that; it is one's "metaphysical well-being and position." It is obviously difficult to encapsulate its full meaning in a translation!] However, if the illness came upon him very suddenly and severely, everyone should visit immediately. Furthermore, even a prestigious person should visit a lesser person. One should visit even many times during the day, even if one is a ben gilo, who removes $\frac{1}{60}$ of the person's illness (Bava Metzia 30b). Anyone who performs more acts of bikur cholim [Ed. note: visits more frequently] is praiseworthy, with the caveat that one avoid burdening the choleh, as mentioned in the previous paragraph.

6. Our rebbi, the Rema, wrote in Se'if 2, "There are those who say that one is permitted to visit a choleh whom he hates. However, this does not appear right to me. He should visit neither cholim nor mourners whom he hates, so that they will not think that he is gloating over their situation and/or does not feel their pain." [Ed.

---
*English adaptation

שהם השונאים [ש"ך סק"ב] אבל שונא שמת יכול ללוותו דבזה לא שייך
שמח לאידו באשר הוא סוף כל האדם [שם] וכן אם השונא שולח לו מקודם
שרוצה לבקרו או לנחמו והוא נותן לו רשות מותר ואדרבא מצד זה נעשה
שלום ביניהם ולכן יש שכתבו שעכשיו נוהגין שהולך השונא דמביא לידי
שלום [באה"ט בשם בה"י וספר החיים ע"ש]:

ז המבקר את החולה לא ישב על גבי מיטה ולא ע"ג כסא ולא על הספסל
אלא מתעטף ויושב לפניו מפני ששכינה למעלה מראשותיו של חולה
[שבת י"ב ב] ודוקא כשהחולה שוכב על הארץ דאז היושב גבוה ממנו
ואין זה מדרך ארץ אבל כששוכב על המיטה מותר לישב על כסא וספסל
וכן המנהג ובזוהר פרשת פנחס מבואר דכשהחולה אדם בינוני לא ישב
לרגליו של חולה דמלאך המות מקומו שם ומראשותיו משמע שם דבכל

───────── Aruch HaShulchan* ─────────

note: The words of the Rema end here.] However, everything is
dependent upon how much hatred is between them (see the Shach,
§2). However, if the hated person himself passes away, certainly one
can escort the funeral procession because there is unquestionably no
happiness on this occasion, for this is the end of all people (see the
Shach there as well). Likewise, if the one who hates a person sends a
message that he would like to visit either the sick or the mourners
toward whom he has enmity, and these individuals allow him to
visit, not only is it permissible — more than that, it is a good thing
because it will generate peace between them. Therefore, there are
those who write that today we have the custom to permit one who
hates another to visit him, since hopefully this will lead to peace
between them (said in the name of the Ba'er Heiteiv and others, see
there).

7. One who visits a choleh should not sit on the bed, on a chair or
on a bench. Instead, he should cloak himself and sit in front of
him, because the Shechinah is at the head of the choleh's bed
(Shabbos 12b). However, this is so only when the choleh is lying on
the floor, because then one who sits on the bed is higher than the
choleh (Ed. note: and thus "higher than the Shechinah") which is
improper. But if the choleh is on a bed, then a visitor is permitted to
sit on a chair or a bench, and this is indeed the custom. The Zohar
(Parashas Pinchas) explains that when an average person becomes
sick, one should not sit at the foot of his bed because the Angel of
Death is there. Furthermore, one should never sit near the head of

*English adaptation

עניין אפילו אינו גבוה מההחולה ואם החולה הוא צדיק גמור לא ישב רק
לרגליו מפני שהשכינה מסבבת אותו מכל צד לבד מרגליו ע"ש:

ח אין מבקרין החולה בג' שעות ראשונות של יום מפני שכל חולה מיקל
עליו המחלה בבוקר ולא יחוש לבקש עליו רחמים ולא בג' שעות
אחרונות של יום שאז מכביד עליו חליו ויתייאש מלבקש עליו רחמים אלא
באמצע היום ואין זה איסור אלא עצה בעלמא לפיכך לא נהגו עתה לדקדק
בזה [נ"ל] וכל מי שביקר את החולה ולא בקש עליו רחמים לא קיים
המצוה:

ט כשמבקש עליו רחמים אם מתפלל שלא בפני החולה לא יתפלל אלא
בלשון הקודש שאין מלאכי השרת מכירין בלשון ארמי אף שהוא קרוב
ללשון הקודש וק"ו בלשונות אחרים ואף שי"א שרק ללשון ארמי אין

Aruch HaShulchan*

the bed, even if one is not higher than the choleh. However, if the
choleh is totally righteous, one should always sit at the foot of the
bed because the Shechinah is everywhere except for the foot of the
bed (see there).

8. One should not visit a choleh during the first three hours of the
day because his illness appears less severe then, so visitors will
not concern themselves with praying for Hashem's mercy on his
behalf [Ed. note: because he appears "too healthy" to need prayers].
Nor should one visit during the last three hours because his illness is
most severe then, so visitors will lose hope and not pray for Hashem's mercy on his behalf [Ed. note: he appears "too sick" for
prayers to be beneficial]. Therefore, one should visit the choleh in
the middle of the day. This is not a prohibition, just sound advice.
Therefore, it seems to me that it is not our custom nowadays to
follow these guidelines meticulously; and anyone who visits the sick
and does not request Hashem's mercy on their behalf has not
fulfilled the mitzvah of bikur cholim.

9. When one requests Hashem's mercy on behalf of a choleh and
one is not praying in his presence, one should pray only in
Hebrew because the angels do not understand Aramaic [Ed. note:
Aramaic was the vernacular in Talmudic times], even though it is
similar to the Hebrew language, nor — kal va'chomer — should one
pray in other languages. And even though there are Sages who say it
is only Aramaic that the angels do not understand, nevertheless,

------

*English adaptation

מזדקקין ולא לשארי לשונות מ"מ וודאי דאפילו לדיעה זו יותר טוב בלשון
הקודש [עי' ט"ז סק"ד] אבל בפני החולה יכול להתפלל בכל לשון שהרי
השכינה שם וכביכול מבקש מלפני השכינה ובהתפלה יכלול אותו בתוך
שארי חולי ישראל שיאמר המקום ירחם עליך בתוך שארי חולי ישראל
דתפלה בעד רבים יותר חשובה כי לא בזה את תפלתם ובשבת אומר שבת
היא מלזעוק ורפואה קרובה לבא ורחמיו מרובין ושבתו בשלום ועי' בא"ח
סי' רפ"ז:

י אומרים לו שיתן דעתו על ענייניו אם הלוה או הפקידו אצלו או שמא יש
לו מה לצוות לזרעו אחריו ולא יפחד מפני זה מהמות אלא כך חובתו של
אדם דאפילו בבריאותו של אדם נכון שיהיו ענייניו מסודרים וכ"ש בחליו
וזהו רצון הבורא יתברך ובזכות זה ישלח לו ד' רפואה שלימה אבל לומר
וידוי לא יזכירו לו כל שאין המחלה תקפתו בחוזק יד ויתבאר בסי' של"ח:

Aruch HaShulchan*
---

even according to this opinion, it is preferable to pray in Hebrew
(see the Taz §4). If one is praying in the choleh's presence, one may
do so in any language because the Shechinah is there. [Ed. note:
Therefore, angelic "assistance" with one's prayers is not necessary.
The exact role of such angelic assistance is a subject of great controversy; suffice it to say that our prayers are always directed to
Hashem.] When praying, one should have in mind all the cholim of
Klal Yisrael by saying, "May Hashem have mercy upon this choleh
among the rest of the cholim of Klal Yisrael," because prayers on
behalf of many are more important and will not be rejected. If one is
visiting a sick person on Shabbos, one should say, "Today is Shabbos, it is an inopportune time to beseech Hashem [Ed. note: i.e., cry
out in supplication], and healing will come shortly. Hashem's mercy
is abundant, and they (the cholim) shall rest peacefully" (see also
Shulchan Aruch, Orach Chaim, Siman 287).

10. Visitors should tell the choleh to apply his mind to weighty
matters. For example, he needs to determine if he has bor-
rowed money, if people have deposited items with him, or if he
perhaps wishes to impart important instructions to his offspring.
Upon hearing these words, he should not fear that he is about to
die. After all, everyone is obligated, even when healthy, to set all his
affairs in order. Certainly, when one is sick, doing so is the will of
the Creator, Blessed be His Name, and in the merit of taking care of
these matters, Hashem will send him a complete healing. However,

---
*English adaptation

יא מבקר איש לאשה ואשה לאיש ובלבד שלא יתייחדו הם לבדם
ומבקרים חולי כותים מפני דרכי שלום ובחולי מעיים ⁻אין האיש
משמש את האשה שלא יבא לידי זרע לבטלה ח״ו אבל האשה משמשת את
האיש אבל שלא בחולי מעיים יכול האיש להקימה ולהשכיבה וכיוצא בזה
יכול לשמשה [ברכ״י ועי׳ ש״ך סק״ט וט״ז סק״ה]:

יב י״א שמי שיש לו חולה בתוך ביתו ילך אצל חכם שבעיר שיבקש עליו
רחמים ושיברכנו וכן נהגו לברך את החולים בבהכ״נ בשעת קריאת
התורה דאז רחמים מתעורר ואם המחלה חזקה משנין השם כלומר

──────── Aruch HaShulchan* ────────

visitors should not advise him to recite Viddui unless his illness is
quite severe, as is explained in Siman 338.

11. A man can visit a woman and a woman can visit a man;
however, they should not be left alone with each other. Also,
one is permitted to visit ill Kusim [Ed. note: a nation of gentiles who
were expelled from their homeland and relocated to Samaria by
King Sancheiriv; this law would apply similarly to any gentile today]
for the sake of peace. Regarding a person with an intestinal illness,
a man should not take care of a woman so that he should not,
heaven forbid, have a seminal discharge [Ed. note: because of improper thoughts or arousal that may occur while providing intimate care
for her]. However, a woman is permitted to take care of a man. If
there is no intestinal illness, then a man is allowed to help a woman
get up and lie down and to offer similar kinds of assistance.

12. There are those who say that one with a sick member in his
household should visit a sage in the city and beseech him to
ask for Hashem's mercy on the choleh's behalf and to bless him.
Indeed, it is also the custom to bless cholim in shul at the time of
the Torah reading because Hashem's attribute of mercy is aroused
at that time. If the sickness is very severe, the custom is to change
the choleh's name; for example, he is given an additional name

*English adaptation

שמוספין לו עוד שם לשמו דזהו אחד מהדברים הקורעים גזר דין של אדם כמו שאמרו חז"ל בר"ה [ט"ז ב] ויש מי שרוצה לומר דכשהחולה במקום אחר לא יתפללו עליו דמי יודע אם הוא חי ולענ"ד לא נהירא כלל שהרי אפילו בגט מחזקינן ליה בחיים דרוב חולים לחיים [גיטין כ"ח א] וכ"ש לעניין תפלה וכן המנהג הפשוט ואין לפקפק בזה כלל וניחום קודם לביקור חולים דזהו חסד עם החיים והמתים וביקור חולים לחיים לבד אבל אם יודע תועלת להחולה בביקור חולים קודם:

──────── Aruch HaShulchan* ────────

because this is one of the ways to nullify a Heavenly decree, as the sages said (Rosh Hashanah 16b). There are those who say that if the choleh is out of the vicinity, one should not pray for him in case he is no longer alive [Ed. note: the concern here is about reciting an unnecessary prayer]. However, in my humble opinion, this is not correct at all because even regarding a bill of divorce sent with an agent to another location, we presume that the person [Ed. note: who sent the bill of divorce] is still alive at the time of its receipt because of the principle that most sick people will live (Gittin 28a). How much more so regarding prayers! Such is our simple custom, and one should not be concerned about this at all. Comforting mourners takes precedence over visiting the sick because comforting mourners is an act of chesed for both the living and the deceased, whereas visiting the sick is only on behalf of the living. However, if one knows of a specific goal to be accomplished by visiting the sick, that goal would take precedence over comforting mourners.

*English adaptation

Shulchan Aruch, Orach Chaim, Siman 287
Comforting Mourners and Visiting the Sick on Shabbos*

1. *One is permitted to comfort mourners on Shabbos. Similarly, one is permitted to visit the sick on Shabbos, but he should not speak to the choleh as he would on a weekday. Instead, he should say, "Shabbos is an inopportune time to beseech Hashem [Ed. note: i.e., beseeching Hashem with supplications], and healing is soon to come. His (Hashem's) mercy is abundant, and may they rest peacefully (on Shabbos)." The Rema adds: And there are those who say that the visitor does not have to state that Hashem's mercy is abundant, etc., and such is the custom (based upon the Rambam, perek 24 [Ed. note: in Hilchos Shabbos; the Rambam, based on verses in Yeshayahu, states that one's speech on Shabbos (under all circumstances) should be different than one's speech on a weekday]).*

————————— **Mishnah Berurah*** —————————

The *Mishnah Berurah,* quoting the *Magen Avraham* and *Shaagas Aryeh,* based on the Gemara (*Shabbos* 12b), states that only with great difficulty did the Rabbis permit comforting mourners and visiting the sick on Shabbos. Therefore, it is not considered proper to visit the sick solely on Shabbos and not to visit on weekdays. The *Mishnah Berurah* further states that we change our wording when wishing the *choleh* a *refuah* on Shabbos to prevent arousing great emotion and crying, which would be forbidden on that day.

In his *Beur Halachah* commentary, the Chofetz Chaim highlights the position of the *Shaarei Teshuvah,* that one who was very busy during the week and did not have an opportunity to visit a dear friend who is ill, yet knows that the *choleh* will receive great comfort from his visit, is in fact performing a mitzvah by visiting and should not stop himself from visiting him on Shabbos and Yom Tov. Similarly, the Chofetz Chaim notes further that if one visited a *choleh* on a weekday, there is no prohibition against visiting him again on Shabbos, since there is no limit to the frequency of bikur cholim. The Rabbis only had reservations about visiting on Shabbos when that was the only day on which one visited, but they had no problem with visiting again on Shabbos. This applies especially if one knows that the *choleh* will be very pleased by, or is in great need of, a Shabbos visit, in which case it is certainly a great mitzvah to pay that visit.

Finally, the *Shaarei Teshuvah* writes that someone who has a delicate nature and would be excessively troubled by a *choleh*'s suffering should not visit him on Shabbos because it would significantly disturb the visitor's *oneg Shabbos* (enjoyment of the Shabbos).

————————

*English adaptation

שלחן ערוך סימן רפז

(א) יכולים לנחם אבלים בשבת וכן יכולים לבקר את החולה ולא יאמר
לו כדרך שאומר לו בחול אלא אומר לו שבת היא מלזעוק ורפואה
קרובה לבא ורחמיו מרובים ושבתו בשלום: הגה וי"א דאין צריך לומר ורחמיו
מרובים וכו' וכן נהגו (רמב"ס פרק כ"ד):

(א) יבולים וכו' — אמרינן בגמרא בקושי
התירו לנחם אבלים ולבקר חולים בשבת
וע"כ לא יפה עושין אותן שכל ימי השבוע אין
הולכין רק בשבת:

(ב) כדרך שאומר לו בחול — דמלטער
ומעורר הבכי דאסור בשבת:

(ג) אומר לו וכו' — אבמקור חולים קאי ובנחום
אבלים יאמר לו שבת היא מלנחם ונחמה
קרובה לבוא ויש מקילים לומר המקום
ינחמך. כתב בפמ"ג אם בא האבל לבהכ"נ אחר
אמירת מזמור שיר ליום השבת שוב לא יקרא השמש
לאו נגד האבל דאין להזכיר אבילות בפרהסיא
ומ"מ לילך בעצמו לו לומר שבת היא לומר מלנחם וכו'
רשאי:

[א*] וכן יכולים לבקר כו' — וכת' במח"ב
שבדעת חכמה כתב לעורר בזה ומה טוב
מנהג ירושלים תוב"ב אם בקורת תהיה לכבוד חתן
או אבי הבן הוא כמו רגע כניסה ויליאה דוקא וגם
כתב בשם חכמי המוסר דמי שספיק בידו לא יפה
עושה לבקר חולה בשבת וילך בחול לבקר עניים
חולים ויראה עניים ונרכם וירחם עליהם כפי אשר
תשיג ידו והוא מצות ב"ח כתקנה כו' ע"ש, ונראה
מי שבזימות החול טריד במילי דשמיא או דעלמא
ובשבת שיש לו פנאי הולך לחולה אותהבו שיודע בו
שיש לו נחת מזה שהוא בא אליו לבקרו מצוה קעביד
ואין לו למנוע מללכת בשבת וי"ט ומי שהוא רך
הלבב ומילר על יסורי החולה אין לו לילך בשבת
לבקר דלטוונג ניתן ולא לצער:

עֲרוּךְ הַשֻּׁלְחָן
אוֹרַח חַיִּים סִימָן רפ"ז

א אָמְרִינַן בְּשַׁבָּת [י"ב.]. דְּבֵית שַׁמַּאי אוֹסְרִין לְנַחֵם אֲבֵלִים וּלְבַקֵּר חוֹלִים בְּשַׁבָּת מִשּׁוּם דְּמִצְטַעֵר [רַשִׁ"י ד"ה] וְאֵין מְנַחֲמִין] וְגַם שֶׁלֹּא יָבֹא לִזְעֹק בְּשַׁבָּת [רִי"ף] וּבֵ"ה מַתִּירִין מִשּׁוּם דְּזֶהוּ בִּכְלָל גמ"ח וְעוֹד שֶׁמֵּקִיל הַצַּעַר מֵהֶם וּבְקֹשִׁי הִתִּירוּ לְנַחֵם אֲבֵלִים וּלְבַקֵּר חוֹלִים בְּשַׁבָּת מִטְּעָמִים שֶׁנִּתְבָּאֲרוּ אֶלָּא שֶׁהִתִּירוּ חֲכָמִים כְּמַ"שׁ הָאָמְנָם אוֹתָם שֶׁבִּימוֹת הַחֹל אֵין הוֹלְכִין רַק בְּשַׁבָּת לֹא יָפֶה הֵם עוֹשִׂים [מג"א] אִם לֹא מִי שֶׁטָּרוּד בִּימוֹת הַחֹל שֶׁא"א לוֹ לֵילֵךְ [ש"ת]:

ב תָּנוּ רַבָּנָן הַנִּכְנָס לְבַקֵּר אֶת הַחוֹלֶה אוֹמֵר שַׁבָּת הִיא מִלִּזְעֹק וּרְפוּאָה קְרוֹבָה לָבֹא בִּזְכוּת הַשַּׁבָּת וִירַחֵיב דַּעְתָּם בְּתַנְחוּמִים [רַשִׁ"י ד"ה שַׁבָּת הִיא] וּמַיְירֵי בְּחוֹלֶה שֶׁאֵין בּוֹ סַכָּנַת הַיּוֹם דְּאִלּוּ יֵשׁ בּוֹ סַכָּנַת הַיּוֹם מוּתָּר

—————— Aruch HaShulchan* ——————

Aruch HaShulchan — Orach Chaim 287
Comforting Mourners and
Visiting the Sick on Shabbos

1. The Gemara (Shabbos 12b) states that Beis Shammai prohibits comforting mourners and visiting the sick on Shabbos because it will cause the visitors too much distress (Rashi) and also because they (the visitors) should not cry out on Shabbos (Rif). Nevertheless, Beis Hillel permits this because it is part of gemilus chassadim and, furthermore, it will lessen the suffering of the sick. However, it was only with great difficulty that the Rabbis permitted comforting mourners and visiting the sick on Shabbos for the reasons just explained. Nevertheless, they did permit it. However, those who do not visit during the week but wait until Shabbos to visit are not acting properly (Magen Avraham), unless they were so busy during the week that they were unable to visit (Shaarei Teshuvah).

2. The Rabbis learned that "one who comes to visit a choleh on Shabbos says: 'Shabbos is not a day for crying, and healing is soon to come in the merit of Shabbos,'" and one should put the choleh at ease with words of comfort (Rashi). This is referring to a

*English adaptation

לזעוק ולהתחנן בשבת כמ"ש בסי' תקע"ו ור"מ אומר שיאמר המבקר
יכולה היא שבת [רי"ף] שתרחם אם תכבדוהו מלהצטער בה [רש"י ד"ה
יכולה] ר' יהודה אומר שיאמר המקום ירחם עליך ועל חולי ישראל דזכות
הרבים גדול ר' יוסי אומר שיאמר המקום ירחם עליך בכלל חולי ישראל
דכשכוללו עם האחרים עדיף טפי שבנא איש ירושלים בכניסתו להחולה
אומר שלום וביציאתו אומר שבת היא מלזעוק ורפואה קרובה לבא ורחמיו
מרובין ושבתו בשלום והרמב"ם פכ"ד [הל' ה'] כתב כלשון הת"ק והטור
והש"ע כתבו כלשון שבנא דלא לחלוק בא אלא להוסיף קצת ומנהגינו
כהרמב"ם וכן כשעושין מי שבירך לחולה בבהכ"נ לא יאמר כמו בחול
המקום ישלח רפואה אלא שבת היא מלזעוק וכו' [הגר"ז] אבל אצלינו

Aruch HaShulchan*
---

sick person whose condition is not life-threatening on that day
because were his condition life-threatening, one would be permitted
to cry out and supplicate on Shabbos, as it states in Siman 576.
Rabbi Meir says that the visitor should inform the choleh that it is
possible that "Shabbos itself will be merciful [Ed. note: i.e., obser-
ving Shabbos will result in Hashem's mercy on your behalf], if you
honor the Shabbos by not crying out on it" (Rashi and the Rif).
Rabbi Yehudah states that one should say, "May Hashem have
mercy on you and on all of the sick of Israel," because the merit of
many is greater. Rabbi Yose says that one should say, "May Hashem
have mercy on you among all the sick of Israel," because when you
include this particular choleh with others, it is far more effective.
Upon entering a choleh's room, Shevnah, the man [Ed. note: a
resident] of Yerushalayim, would say, "Peace," and upon leaving,
he would say, "Today is Shabbos and therefore we cannot cry out.
Healing will certainly come soon, Hashem's mercy is abundant and
you shall rest on Shabbos in peace." The Rambam (Hilchos Shabbos
perek 24) wrote in accordance with the first version. The Tur in the
Shulchan Aruch wrote in accordance with the wording of Shevnah,
who did not come to argue with the Tanna Kamma, but to slightly
expand on his words. Our minhag (custom) is to follow the Rambam
and this is what we do on Shabbos when we make a mi shebeirach
for a choleh in shul: We do not use the weekday wording, that
"Hashem should grant a refuah," but rather we say, "Today is
Shabbos and therefore we cannot cry out," etc. Nevertheless, we
recite the mi shebeirach with the following statement: "And Hashem should send him a refuah shleimah," etc., followed by "It is

---
*English adaptation

מברכים וישלח לו רפואה שלימה וכו' שבת היא מלזעוק וכו' וכן נדפס
בסידורים ולא ידעתי מי התיר להם זה אם לא בחולה מסוכן גדול שיש בו
סכנת היום כמ"ש:

ג ולא הזכיר הש"ס איזה לשון לומר בניחום אבלים ונראה דיכול לומר
כמו בחול המקום ינחמך בתוך וכו' אבל י"א שי"ל כמו בחולה שבת
היא מלנחם ונחמה קרובה לבא ורחמיו מרובין ושבתו בשלום [רש"ל
וב"ח] וע' ביו"ד סי' שצ"ג ואצלינו לא נהגו בניחום אבלים בשבת:

Shabbos and we cannot cry out," etc. This is written in the siddurim,
and I do not know who provided this leniency to allow them to do
this, unless it is only with regard to a seriously ill person in great
danger of dying on that very day, as I stated previously.

[Ed. note: Se'if 3, which is the final se'if in this siman, deals with
nichum aveilim (comforting mourners) and will not be translated
here.]

*English adaptation

◆§ Additional Talmudic and Midrashic Sources

1) *Mesechtos Ketanos*: *Maseches Avos d'Rebbi Nassan, perek* 30: Comforting mourners, visiting the sick and performing *chesed* bring good to the world.

2) *Maseches Semachos*: *Perek* 1, Halachah 1: The performance of bikur cholim has no limit.

3) *Maseches Shabbos* (127a): Rabbi Yochanan states that there are six precepts from whose performance one benefits in this world and whose principal remains undiminished in the World to Come. They are: hospitality; visiting the sick; praying with introspection; waking up early to learn in the *beis midrash* (Rabbi Yaakov Emden says it means bringing others to the *beis midrash*); raising one's children to learn Torah; and judging one's friend favorably. Rashi (127b) adds that bikur cholim is a component of *gemilus chassadim*.

4) *Maseches Bava Kamma* (100a): Rabbi Yose expounded on *Shemos* 18:20: "And you shall make known to them the path on which they shall travel and the action that they should do." The "path" refers to the performance of *gemilus chassadim*, and "on which they shall travel" refers to the performance of bikur cholim. [Ed. note: There are many other passages of a similar nature, expounded upon in a comparable fashion, which we do not list here.]

5) *Otzar HaMidrashim*: *Chupas Eliyahu* 174: We derive bikur cholim from *Bereishis* 18:1: "And Hashem appeared to him [Ed. note: Avraham] in Eilonei Mamrei." Hashem came to perform the mitzvah of bikur cholim, and since we are obligated to emulate Hashem, we too must perform acts of bikur cholim.

This volume is part of
THE ARTSCROLL SERIES®
an ongoing project of
translations, commentaries and expositions
on Scripture, Mishnah, Talmud, Halachah,
liturgy, history, the classic Rabbinic writings,
biographies and thought.

For a brochure of current publications
visit your local Hebrew bookseller
or contact the publisher:

Mesorah Publications, ltd

4401 Second Avenue
Brooklyn, New York 11232
(718) 921-9000
www.artscroll.com